SUSS
CARPING

Clive Williams

Sussex Carping by Clive Williams.

Published in 2011 by Freebird Publishing

☎ 01293 415339 or 07941 637336

© Freebird Publishing

Edited & proofed by Keith Jenkins
Map Illustrations by Suzanne Lane
Layout and Design by Cathy Card
Print Management by Linda Jenkins
Most photography supplied.

Printed in Great Britain by
Printwize Interact Marketing Services Ltd
9 Stepfield, Witham, Essex CM8 3BN

CONTENTS

Introduction and Acknowledgements

Firstly, I hope you find this book both useful and interesting. It began life as just a thought but, as I looked harder and harder at what is on offer for the Carp Angler from, or visiting, the fabulous county of Sussex, I realised that we had more than most of us knew about, myself included. To that end I felt that there was a place on the bookshelf for a book like this.

As I've said, the more I looked the more I was surprised at what was available, and not just exclusive little syndicates, but also lovely day ticket pools set in the most beautiful countryside. I have tried to be as comprehensive and accurate as possible with the information given and have personally contacted everybody within these pages about their waters. Owners, secretaries, club officials and bailiffs have been very helpful and I would like to thank them all for the time spent answering all of my questions. As with anything like this, there are bound to be fisheries and lakes that I've missed, and apologies to those of you that fall into that category, but there was only so much that I could do – maybe if enough people contact me it will soon be time for Volume Two!

Please use this book as it is intended to be – a guide. Waters change, often very quickly. What might have been a 25lb mirror when we went to press could well be a thirty next Spring. Conversely, big fish die, so bear that in mind. The costs for angling for them could also change quickly, especially in the present financial climate, so before any money changes hands, or any journeys are undertaken, it may well be worth using the contact details listed to ensure everything is as we have written.

Finally, a few thank you's.

To all the retail tackle shops, and the tackle companies, who have taken out adverts; please support them.

Monster respect to all the friends who chipped in with their 'carp tips'.

A massive thanks to Keith and Linda at Freebird for their willingness to listen, their support and their tireless commitment to making this book as excellent as it is (hopefully, we'll be working together again soon).

Finally, a special thank you to all the Sussex carpers who contributed an article, just to make the book a little different and more enjoyable, and also to confirm what is available for anglers in Sussex.

Happy Carping
Clive Williams
Nov 2011

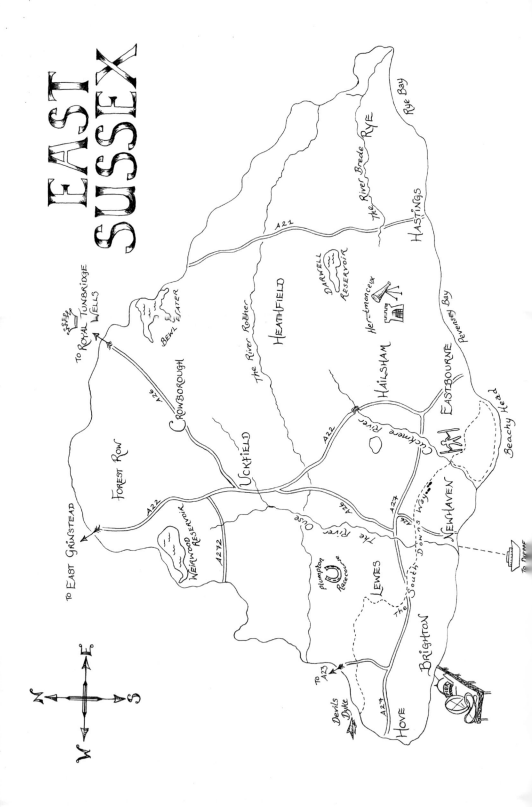

Contents

Amazon Wood Fishery
Day Ticket – East Sussex

Address
BN27 3EQ

Contact Details
Mr Ian Smith
☎ 01323 449502

Nearest Main Town
Eastbourne

Opening Hours
7.30am to 6pm

Costs
To fish Badger Lake you have to be a member. The cost of membership is £25 and runs for 12 months.

The cost for a 24 hour session is £15 for 3 rods.

Day tickets on both Fox & Rabbit cost £7 for 2 rods.

24 hours members only – £12 for 2 rods only.

Juniors, OAP's & disabled day tickets cost £4 for 2 rods.

Facilities

Carp Size

32lb

The Fishery

This is a three lake complex sitting in 20 acres of peaceful woodlands. A few years ago it was a series of 8 old brick pits until the owner transformed the overgrown pits into three, highly prolific and highly stocked small lakes.

Directions

The complex is off Summerhill Lane which is situated off the southbound A22 just outside Polegate in the east of the county. There is a fishery signpost in the lane. Drive past the cement factory and the two day ticket waters until you come to the car park.

The Lakes

Fox Lake (Day Ticket)

This is the first lake of the two day ticket waters that you will see when you enter the fishery. The lake is a rectangular 1 acre pit with the banks surrounded by shrubs and reeds. There are 9 flat, gravelled swims. The water on Fox is a colourful orange, clay colour and the depths range from 3 to 6 feet.

Carp Stocks

Commons to 18lb+, mirrors to 20lb+, leather and ghost to double figures.

The carp in this fishery have bred like wildfire and as there is only a low stock of predators, the carp stocks run well into the high 100's, from those in the ounces to 20lb+ fish.

Rabbit Lake (Day Ticket)

This lake is on the left hand side of the track, opposite Fox. It is an oval shaped pool just over 1 acre in size and features include reeds and shrubs on the banks, whilst the lake has lily pads and a small island which can be reached via a bridge and fished. The water is rich in colour and the depths range between 3 to 6 feet.

Carp Stocks

Commons to 19lb, mirrors to almost 20lb, leather and ghost to double figures.

Estimated total stocks as Fox Lake.

Badger Lake (Members Only)

Badger is the final lake on the complex and is tucked away from both the other waters. This 2 acre lake offers fishing in the isolation of the surrounding woodlands. Only 4 well spread swims are available and one is a double, these swims are flat, gravelled and comfortable. The lake is packed with features, 2 islands, lily pads, weed beds and depths of 6 to 12 feet.

Carp Stocks

Commons to 23lb+, mirrors to 32lb+, leather, ghost and Koi to double figures. This lake is stocked with Mark Simmonds' Fisher's Pond English carp.

For more information on fishing this lake contact the owner.

Fishery Rules

Barbless hooks only. No carp sacks, peanuts or fixed leads. All litter must be removed from the complex. Unhooking mats must be used. Juniors under 16 years old must be accompanied by an adult.

Additional Information

No close season.

Bait boats allowed on Badger Lake only.

All three lakes hold crucians to over 3lb. Other species include silver bream, perch, roach, rudd, tench and some big eels.

Barrets Park Farm
Day Ticket – East Sussex

Address
TN21 8QS

Contact Details
Mr Richard Leeves
☎ 01435 863668

Nearest Main Town
Heathfield

Opening Hours
Dawn to dusk

Costs
Day tickets
Adults £5
Juniors £2.50
Up to 3 rods

24 hour ticket
Adults £10
Juniors £5
Up to 3 rods

Night fishing must be booked
in advance. Pay on bank.

Facilities

New toilet is planned
(current one is basic)

Carp Size

The Fishery

This century's old fishery was once a reservoir for iron workings. Formally known as Bojos lakes and situated on farmland in Old Heathfield.

Directions

Located in Weaversbrook Lane, Heathfield. Look for the B2203 in Heathfield and after about ½ mile, turn left into Park Road. The wall of Heathfield Park should be on your left. Carry on until Sandy Cross Lane joins from the right, at which point you should see an oak tree on a small island in the road. Leaving the lane at this oak tree, follow the lane until you pass a large house on the right. Turn right into RFM Coach Works and follow the lane through the farm until you come to the car park.

The Lakes

Top Lake

The Top Lake is a secluded oval shaped water of almost 3 acres. Features include lily pads and reeds in depths up to 5 feet. There are 20 swims on the lake.

Carp Stocks

Commons and mirrors to 20lb+. Total stock is unknown, but it does hold a good head of fish.

Bottom Lake

This is a sheltered, picturesque water of ½ an acre which is round in shape. It has depths of between 5 to 6 feet, a scattering of lily pads and 7 swims.

Carp Stocks

Commons to 20lb+, mirrors to 25lb+. Total stock is unknown.

Fishery Rules

Barbless hooks only. No carp sacks. Unhooking mats must be used. No fixed leads. No litter. Bait boats allowed. No bait bans.

Additional Information

Open all year. Disabled access is not good. Other species include roach, rudd, tench, some very big perch and a few crucians. That most famous angler, Chris Yates, has fished this water.

> Choose bait that you have confidence in and persist with it. Changing baits every other weekend is not the way forward
>
> Bill Cottam

Belfry Coarse Fishery
Day Ticket – East Sussex

Address
BN27 4DU

Contact Details
Mr Wilkinson
☎ 07967 557632

Nearest Main Town
Hailsham

Opening Hours
7am to 5pm

Costs
Day tickets
Adults £6
Juniors, OAP's £5

24 hour ticket
Adult £13
Juniors, OAP's £10

Prices are for 2 rods

Facilities

Both lakes have a toilet.
The owner will supply water
(no tap)

Carp Size

The Fishery

Belfry is located on a quiet farm just off the A22 near Hailsham. Both lakes are in open fields.

Directions

On the A22 north of Hailsham look for the Boship roundabout. This is a large roundabout that has a petrol station and food outlet adjacent. Take the exit for Horam, which is the A267 and after about ¾ of a mile the signposted fishery is on the left.

The Lakes

Belfry Lake

This is the larger of the two waters at almost 2 acres and has an island in the middle. Depths range from 6 to 8 feet and there are small patches of lilies and reeds. 20 swims sit amongst some flat grassed and sloped swims.

Carp Stocks

Mirrors and commons to 25lb+

Estimated total stock unknown, but lots of doubles.

Belfry pond

A small, oval shaped water of less than an acre, situated in the middle of open farmland. There are a few overhanging trees and bushes along the banks, and a scattering of reeds in the margins. This clay bottomed lake has depths from 4 to 6 feet and just 5 swims. This lake has less stock than the bigger lake and is more difficult to fish.

Belfry Coarse Fishery
Day Ticket – East Sussex

Carp Stocks
Mirrors and commons to 25lb+
Estimated total stock unknown.

Fishery Rules
Barbless hooks only. No carp sacks. No nut baits. Unhooking mats must be used. Bait boats are allowed.

Additional Information
This is a 2 rod only fishery. Open all year. Night fishing is possible. Not suitable for the disabled angler.

> It's so important to be up at first light as often the fish will show in areas they might be feeding
>
> Ben Hamilton

Churchsettle Farm Fishery
Day Ticket – East Sussex

Address
TN5 6NH

Contact Details
Mr Chris Velten
☎ 01892 783386

Nearest Main Town
Wadhurst

Opening Hours
Dawn to dusk

Costs
All costs will be given when fishing is booked.

Facilities

Carp Size

20lb+

The Fishery

Privately owned fishery that has been established since 1993, a secluded and picturesque lake located in the countryside. Lake is open all year.

Directions

Travelling from Tonbridge on the A21 turn right onto B2162 to the village of Lamberhurst. Then onto the A2100 towards Wadhurst. At Wadhurst turn left onto the B2099 heading towards Ticehurst. After a mile turn right down Stonegate Road, then look for Churchsettle Lane, which is on the right. Fishery entrance is on the left down this lane.

The Lake

This clay bottomed water is approximately 2 acres in size. Depths go to a maximum of 6 feet and only 6 anglers are allowed at any time. The lake is surrounded by trees and does have a few lily pads, but it is weed free.

Carp Stocks

Commons and mirrors to 20lb+. Total stock is unknown but does hold a fair number of fish.

Fishery Rules

Barbless hooks only. Unhooking mats must be used. All fish must be treated with respect.

Additional Information

This is a day ticket only fishery, open from dawn to dusk. Booking is advisable due to the limited number of anglers allowed. Up to 3 rods can be used.

THE TACKLE WAREHOUSE LTD

Unit 14-16, Rutherford Way, Crawley,
West Sussex, RH10 9RD
Telephone Hotline: 01293 550907
Website: www.thetacklewarehouseltd.co.uk
Email: john@thetacklewarehouseltd.co.uk

THE TACKLE WAREHOUSE LTD.

THE TACKLE WAREHOUSE

n Aladdin's cave of carp fishing tackle

he Tackle Warehouse is a fishing tackle shop like you've never seen before… once you've found it! Hidden away in Crawley, West Sussex, Tackle Warehouse has three floors that ver carp fishing predominantly, but t's not to say that coarse and match ing tackle, plus fly and sea fishing gear n't more than adequately stocked too. With permanent bivvy and bedchair plays, a walk-in bait room that's the size a small shop on its own, and a quality thing area, this labyrinth of tackle is a den gem – but once you've discovered ou'll never go anywhere else!

ackle Warehouse has an easy layout customers can freely browse without sman pressure, but there are five very perienced and friendly members of f on hand to help and advise you if uired, particularly on the many local o fishing venues and methods.

ree tea and coffee are on hand while visit – you may even get a biscuit if u're lucky –to make this the full 'tackle p experience'.

Now in its third year, the Tackle rehouse has plenty of open days planned throughout the year. The first of these will feature expert carper Rob Maylin plus a 'surprise guest', although it;s a bit of a secret who this is at this time.

For customers who aren't quite local enough to visit, the website is being updated and revamped, and will soon be available for mail-order shopping. Plus, in the unlikely event you want something that for some reason isn't in stock, the staff will get it in for you, and at a fair, competitive price. With a no-quibble returns policy, the customer is definitely always right at this shop!

The Tackle Warehouse is pleased to be the exclusive European stockist for Saxon rods – these high-end carp wands are virtually custom-built on some of the thinnest blanks available. They're thoroughly recommended, but be careful when you give them a waggle – you may never be the same again!

The only real way to discover this gem is to experience it for yourself – their opening hours and directions are below. We hope to see you there!

AMONG THE TACKLE BRANDS STOCKED ARE:
Korda / **Gardner** / ESP / **Kryston** / Avid / **Solar** / Jag / **Sonik** / ACE
himano / Thinking Anglers / **Maver** / Nash / **Fox** / Rig Master / **Enterprise**

BAIT BRANDS INCLUDE:
CCmoore / **Mainline** / Nash / **Dynamite** / Carp Company / **Sonubaits**
Plus fresh maggots, casters and worms always available

OPEN
Monday to Wednesday 9am to 5.30pm
Thursday 9am to 9pm (late night)
Friday 9am to 6pm
Saturday 7.30am to 5.30pm
Sunday 7.30 to 1pm

Falkenvil Fishery
Day Ticket – East Sussex

Address
BN27 2RJ

Contact Details
General enquires
☎ 01323 849057

Specimen Lake bookings
call Keith Knight
☎ 07766 135836

All other bookings
call Roland Knight
☎ 07867 526753

info@falkenvilfishery.co.uk
www.falkenvilfishery.co.uk

Nearest Main Town
Hailsham

Opening Hours
Day & Specimen – Dawn
to dusk
Evening – Last 4 hours of
daylight

Costs
General day tickets on Main
& Match Lakes 1, 2 & 3
Adults – 1 rod £8
2 rods £10
Juniors – 1 rod £7
2 rods £8
Evening 4 hour tickets – £5
all anglers.

Specimen Lake
Adult ticket – 3 rods £15
A specimen ticket entitles
fishing on any of the lakes.

Facilities

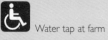 Water tap at farm

Carp Size

30lb+

The Fishery
This fishery is situated in the heart of the east of the county, between Hailsham and Eastbourne. The five lakes are heavily stocked, which provide superb fishing for match, novice and specimen anglers. This is a day only fishery.

Directions
Heading towards Hailsham on the A22 look for the Arlington Eagles roundabout. Take the A295 towards Hailsham and follow this road for 0.6 miles to the mini roundabout which is next to a petrol station. Turn right onto the B2104 which is Ersham Road. Follow for exactly 1 mile then turn left into Saltmarsh Lane. The fishery entrance is 0.3 miles on the left hand side.

The Lakes
Main Lake
This 4 acre water which has an island is between 3 to 7 feet deep. Weed free. 8 flat swims only.

Carp stocks
Commons to 20lb+, mirrors and fully scaled to 21lb+. Described as holding hundreds of fish.

Specimen Lake
2 acres in size with a large island and only 5 swims. Shallow areas of 3 feet and other depths of 8 feet. Weed free but lily pads are present. Lots of bankside trees. Swims on this lake must be reserved. Boilies allowed on this lake.

Carp stocks

Commons to 30lb+, mirrors to 25lb, ghost to 18lb and 4 albino grass carp to 18lb. Estimated total stock 65 fish

Match Lakes 1, 2 and 3.

Although these three waters are described as match lakes they all contain a lot of carp. Match 1 is 4 acres and home to commons to 14lb and mirrors to 12lb. Match 2 is ½ an acre with lots of single figure fish. Match 3 is 2 acres and has mirrors to 13lb and commons to 14lb. All three lakes are weed free and have depths that average 7 feet. The average size of the fish is 6lb with hundreds of them in all three waters.

Fishery Rules

Strictly no night fishing. No boilies except on Specimen Lake. No plastic baits or nut baits. Barbless hooks only. No carp sacks, fixed leads or lead core. Unhooking mats must be used. No dogs or fires. Rods not to be left unattended. Under16's must be accompanied by an adult. All litter to be put in the bins provided.

Additional Specimen Lake Rules.

All swims must be booked. Minimum 12lb main line. 42 inch landing net must be used. Large mats to be used. No under 16's allowed. All cars to be parked in the parking area.

Note – fish in this lake have been micro tagged.

Additional Information

Fishery operates a close season between 1st April to 16th June.

Bait boats allowed. Disabled access, weather permitting. Other species include bream, chub, roach, rudd, tench, barbel and big catfish in the Specimen Lake.

Framfield Park Fishery
Day Ticket – East Sussex

Address
TN22 5QJ

Contact Details
Chris
☎ 01825 890948 or
07798 751175

Nearest Main Town
Uckfield

Opening Hours
7am to dusk

Costs
Day ticket on Brookhouse
& Spring Lakes – Adult £8
Junior & OAP £6. 2 rods.
Evening tickets are available.

Burywood Lake must be
booked in advance and
prices are given when you
book. 3 rods allowed on
this lake.

Facilities

Carp Size

The Fishery

This three lake complex was established in 1992 and although all the lakes
contain carp, it has one which is specifically for the specimen hunter.

Directions

Situated a couple of miles off the A22, south of Uckfield. 3 miles past Uckfield
turn left onto the Eastbourne Road towards Framfield. After a mile take a right
onto High Cross Lane, which leads onto Brookhouse Lane. The fishery is a mile
further, on the left.

The Lakes

Spring Lake

This is a 3 acre spring fed water with an average depth of 4 feet. It has two
central islands and 36 swims. No weed but lily pads.

Carp Stocks

Mirrors, commons and ghosties to mid doubles. Grass carp to 23lb. Total stock
is unknown.

Brookhouse Lake

Similar in construction to Spring Lake, only a little smaller at 2½ acres. Again
spring fed with depths to 4 feet and weed free apart from some lilies. Two
islands. 36 swims.

Carp Stocks

Commons and mirrors to 18lb+. Total stock is unknown.

Burywood Lake

Around the same size as Brookhouse, only a different shape. Located on a hillside and surrounded on one side by woodlands, this is a deeper water with depths of 10 feet. It has an island at one end and, like the others, is weed free, but with some lily pads.

Carp Stocks

Commons to 28lb, mirrors to 25lb. Total stock is unknown.

Fishery Rules

Barbless hooks only. No carp sacks. Unhooking mats must be used. All landing nets must be dipped before use. No trout pellets, nuts of any kind or particles. No bait boats.

Note: Brookhouse and Spring Lakes are day fishing only. Night fishing is allowed on Burywood Lake only.

Additional Information

Open all year. All lakes are easily accessible with constructed pathways and purpose built flat swims. Disabled facilities are available. Brookhouse and Spring contain roach, tench, bream, perch and crucians. Burywood is home to some catfish which go over 50lbs.

Address
TN3 9AP

Contact Details
Venue office
☎ 01892 616424
Head bailiff – Ian Ludman

fishfrant@gmail.com

www.frantlakes.com

Nearest Main Town
Tunbridge Wells

Opening Hours
Day & Specimen 7am to 5pm
Overnight 5pm to 7am

Costs
Main lakes
Day tickets
Adults – 1 rod £8, 2 rods £12
Juniors – 1 rod £6, 2 rods £7
Same price for OAP/disabled.

Day & night – 2 rods
Adults £22
Juniors £12

Specimen lakes
Day tickets – 3 rods £17

24 hours – 3 rods £30

No concessions.

Overnight tickets are available.

Facilities

This complex has tarmac roadways

Carp Size

31lb

The Fishery

A privately owned complex of 8 lakes near to the Kent border, set in 200 acres of peaceful parkland and surrounded by mature trees. Established in the eighties, this venue offers something for all types of coarse fishing, including some big carp. Open all year round. Day and night tickets are available.

Directions

About a 40 minute drive from South London on the A21, a couple of miles south of Tunbridge Wells, just inside the Sussex border. The fishery is on the Hawkenbury Road near the village of Bells Yew Green.

The Lakes

Skirmish (1) and Horseshoe (6)

Described as match lakes on the quiet side of the complex, Skirmish is 1½ acres with depths of 4 to 8 feet and no weed, 20 swims and lots of silver fish. Also present are commons to 20lb+ and an unusual black leather of 20lb. Skirmish has one island.

Horseshoe is around 2 acres in size and also holds mirrors and commons to 20lb+. Both waters hold plenty of roach, bream, tench and perch. 2 rods only.

Stumps (2)

A shallow lake of 1½ acres with no weed except for some lily pads. Maximum depth is just over 3 feet. 20 flat grass bank swims and a good surface fishing water during the summer. Contains ghost and Koi carp and mirrors and commons to 20lb. Other species include roach, tench, bream and crucian carp. 2 rods only.

Sunken Island (3) and Car Park Lake (4)

The largest of the six lakes on the main part of the site, these are actually one lake divided by a causeway and wooden bridge. Close to the car parks, these waters hold the biggest head of carp on the complex and are described as runs waters. Both waters are 2½ acres in size with depths between 4 to 6 feet. Weed free except for some lily pads on the Car Park Lake, they have produced commons to 31lb. There are lots of commons and mirrors, plus silver fish. 2 rods only.

Waterfall (5)

A small lake of ½ an acre and heavily stocked with all sorts of fish including commons and mirrors up to 18lb+. Depths range between 4 to 5 feet with 8 swims available, a popular water and good for a run or two, described as an ideal junior lake. 2 rods only.

Snags Lake (7)

Described as a specimen lake and set away from the main lakes, this water covers 3½ acres with depths up to 8 feet although it does have shallower areas of 4 feet plus 2 islands, weed and lily beds. The centre of this lake has some harsh tree snags. Holds stocks of roach, bream, tench and perch. Also present are commons and mirrors to 30lb+ and crucian carp to over 4lb. Up to 3 rods allowed.

Lake 8 (No Name)

Just like Snags Lake, this 2 acre weed free water has some wicked snags running through its middle. Stocked with plenty of 20lb+ commons and mirrors. Depths range between 4 to 8 feet and like all the complexes waters, the bottom is firm clay/sandstone. Biggest common goes 28lb and mirror stands at 30lb+.

Fishery Rules

A whole list of rules for the fish, the angler and the property are listed on the website.

Basic carp fishing rules. Barbless hooks only. Unhooking mats must be used and not shared. No braided line. Minimum 36" landing net. No bait boats. No fires. No dogs. No litter.

Additional Information.

Junior anglers are not allowed to fish the specimen lakes and must be accompanied by an adult at all times on the other lakes.

Disposable type bar-b-ques are allowed, although hot food is available from Friday evening all through the weekend. Hot food must be booked.

Complex has entry security office and barriers.

Trailer service is available for the specimen lakes. Part of the River Teise runs beside the specimen lakes and is fishable, holding carp to 15lb+.

Horam Manor Fishery
Day Ticket – East Sussex

Address
BN27 1HY

Contact Details
Graham
☎ 01323 840889
or 0770 7759364

www.hmffisheries.co.uk

Nearest Main Town
Heathfield

Opening Hours
Dawn to dusk

Costs
£5 per rod

Annual day ticket
1 rod £80, 2 rods £120

24 hour ticket £15 2 rods
Extra rod £5

Night fishing must be booked in advance.

Facilities

Carp Size

25lb+

The Fishery

Horam Manor fishery is a family owned fishery on part of the historic, 300 acre estate. The ponds were once open cast mines and the majority of the lakes are set in the wooded areas of the complex. The owners describe it as a place for a great family day out.

Directions

Easy to find once you get to the village of Horam. Heading south from the village on the A267, turn right at the signposted entrance to "Horam Manor" about ½ a mile from Horam. Follow the access road past the caravan site until you come to the fishery car park.

The Lakes

In all there are ten small lakes that all contain carp to double figures with some lakes home to 20lb+ fish.

House Pond, The Nursery and Great Pond.

These ponds (biggest 1 acre) are very close to the car park and toilets. Depths vary from 3 to 5 feet and on the Great Pond there is an island, lily pads, weed beds and reeds. No night fishing is allowed on these ponds. Suitable for the disabled angler.

Carp Stocks

Commons and mirrors to 14lb. Total stock unknown

Banky Fork

½ acre in size, 7 feet deep, with commons, mirrors and leathers to over 12lb.

Long Water
½ acre in size, 12 feet deep, with commons and mirrors to 10lb+.

Brook Pit
Small, oval shaped pool, 3 to 7 feet deep, with fish to over double figures.

Coney
½ acre in size and 3 to 6 feet deep with fish to double figures.

Catchpool
The most recently restored pond and, as the name suggests, stocked with large numbers of small fish including commons and mirrors to 10lb+. 3 to 6 feet deep.

Lagoon and Clearhedges
Both these lakes are about 1 acre in size and the furthest walk from the car park. Features include lily pads and reed beds. These both contain carp to over 25lb. Total stock in the above 7 ponds is unknown.

Fishery Rules
Barbless hooks only. No keep nets. No carp sacks. No bait boats. No bait bans.

Additional Information
Open all year, other species in most lakes include crucians, roach, rudd, tench, bream and eels.

Iden Wood Fishery
Day Ticket – East Sussex

Address
TN31 7UT

Contact Details
Andy Ashdown
☎ 01797 280180 or
07906 232225

Nearest Main Town
Rye

Opening Hours
Dawn to dusk

Costs
Day tickets
£8 – 2 rods, £10 – 3 rods
Evening ticket – £4

24 hour ticket
£14 – 2 rods
£16 – 3 rods

48 hour ticket
£22 – 2 rods
£24 – 3 rods

Concessions for OAP's
& Juniors

Facilities

Carp Size

30lb+

The Fishery

This well established fishery consists of four man-made lakes and two natural waters. Very flexible tickets are available for those who want to fish for only an evening or those who want to fish for the weekend. The fishery is described as disabled friendly.

Directions

The fishery is located in Iden Wood, just off Coldharbour Lane, which runs between the Rye Road in Peasmarsh and Iden. The entrance is to be found on the left if you are travelling from the Peasmarsh end of Coldharbour Lane.

The Lakes

Match Lake

As the name suggests this 3 acre water holds lots of species other than carp. It has 20 flat swims that are raised from the waters edge. Depths range from 3 feet down to 12 feet. There are overhanging trees, bushes and an island. The lake is weed free.

Carp Stocks

Mirrors to 30lb, commons to 20lb+

Estimated total stock – High numbers of doubles and a good few over 20lb.

Spring Lake

Located just above the Match Lake. At 1½ acres with depths of 3 feet to 10 feet it is considered an ideal water for the beginner.

Carp Stocks

Biggest mirror goes 18lb.

Estimated total stock – 100+ fish.

Middle Lake

This is a contoured, 2 to 3 acre water which is man-made. It is almost two separate lakes which are joined in the centre by a channel. Maximum depth is 4½ feet. There are 25 swims that are generally flat, although some have platforms.

Carp Stocks

Only small fish to 5lb

Specimen Lake

This is a natural 3 acre lake with depths of 4 to 12 feet. It is oval shaped and open. Features include an island, reed beds and some overhanging trees and bushes. There are 25 flat swims and platforms.

Carp Stocks

Commons to 25lb, mirrors to 33lb including a leather of 28lb.

Estimated total stock – 200+ fish.

Orchard Lake

This 1 acre lake is the longest walk from the car park. Depths of 3 to 5 feet. No weed. The average size of the carp is between 12lb and 15lb, although it is known to hold at least a couple of twenties.

Tench Lake

The name speaks for itself.

Fishery Rules

No boilies, nuts or trout pellets. No carp sacks or fixed leads. Barbless hooks only. Unhooking mats must be used. No dogs or fires. All litter to be removed from fishery. Under 16's must be accompanied by an adult. Bait boats not allowed.

Additional Information

Maximum fishing time is 48 hours. Parking is allowed next to all lakes except Orchard. All waters are clay bottomed. Open all year. Other species present include tench, roach, perch, rudd, gudgeon and eels.

> On busy waters I find turning up late evening better than first light as I can drop onto showing fish and the cover of darkness gives me a better chance
>
> Nick Helleur

Mayfly Aquacare
Day Ticket – East Sussex

Address
BN8 6BY

Contact Details
Miles Gosling
☎ 01323 811025 or
07974 766674

www.mayflyaquacare.co.uk

Nearest Main Town
Lewes

Opening Hours
7am to 1 hour before dusk

Costs
Longreed
Adult – 2 rods £12
OAP's & under 14's – £8

Ashreed
Adult – 1 rod £7, 2 rods £10
OAP's – 1 rod £5, 2 rods £7

Under 14's free

Facilities

Tackle trolley's, and for the disabled, a quad bike is available. Fishery hut.

Carp Size

Longreed and Ashreed Lakes

The Fishery

Mayfly Aquacare are a fishery management company whose portfolio includes pond and lake construction, aquatic plants, fish rearing and two lakes open for fishing.

Directions

The lakes are situated near the town of Lewes at Laughton on the B2124 More precise directions are given when you phone to make a booking.

The Lakes

Ashreed Lake

This is a mixed coarse fishery of 1 acre and has 15 swims. There are two islands with depths of two feet in the reed fringed bays, down to six feet in the central channel. There are also numerous lily beds.

Carp Stocks

Commons to 21lb, mirrors to 17lb.

Longreed Lake

Longreed is a 1½ acre carp water that is packed with features. There are three islands, numerous lily beds and marginal reeds amongst the 7 swims. There are also silt beds, clay bars and plateaux. Depths reach 7 feet but the average is 4 to 5 feet.

Carp Stocks

Commons to 31lb+, mirrors to 34lb+. Total stock unkown

Fishery Rules

Landing nets, weigh slings and unhooking mats are all supplied. No carp sacks. Barbless hooks only. No fixed leads/method rigs. No dogs, fires, litter or radios. No bait boats. Fishing from designated swims only. No rods to be left unattended. Nobody under the age of 14 unless accompanied by an adult. This is a 2 rod only fishery.

Additional Information

Open all year. Bookings only. No night fishing. Fishing hut available for club and match bookings.

Merricks Fishery
Day Ticket – East Sussex

Address
Icklesham

Contact Details
Mr Terry Betson
☎ 01424 812905

Nearest Main Town
Hastings

Opening Hours
Dawn to dusk

Costs
Day tickets – All £8
No concessions.

Facilities

Carp Size

38lb

The Fishery

A private fishery on farmland set in peaceful rural surroundings.

The lake was dug as a reservoir in 1945 to hold water supplies for the farm.

Directions

Approximately half way between Hastings and Rye and just off the A259. From Hastings go through the villages of Guestling Green and Guestling Thorn on the A259 towards Rye. Just before the village of Icklesham look for a turning on the left which is Broad Street. Follow this road for about 1000 yards until you come to 2 small cottages either side of the road. The lake car park is next to the cottage on the left. The water can be seen from the car park.

The Lake

A triangular shaped lake of just over 1½ acres, set at the foot of farm fields with woods on one side and many overhanging trees and bushes. There are 8 grass banked swims and the average depth is 6 feet with a deeper area going down to 13 feet towards the dam end. Merricks was stocked in 1993 with carp from Hawkhurst Fish Farm and many are zip linears. The water is clay bottomed and weed free. Well stocked with commons to 33lb and mirrors to 38lb. In total there are 3 known fish over 30lb and at least 18 fish over 20lb. The water holds a true, scale-less leather, and ghost carp to over 20lb. Estimated total stock is over 100 fish.

Fishery Rules

Barbless hooks only. Unhooking mats must be used. Rods not to be left unattended. No excessive groundbaiting. No dogs, fires, or litter. No carp sacks. 2 rods only (3 rods at the bailiff's discretion). Bait boats are allowed.

Additional Information.

A small number of season tickets will be made available for the 2011 season. These tickets will allow night fishing for a maximum stay of 48 hours, prices on application. Not suitable for the disabled angler as the lake is at the bottom of a sloped field. Other species include roach, rudd and crucian carp. This water is tea coloured and the carp feed by smell so strong flavoured baits work well.

To sink your line fast, pour diluted washing up liquid on the spool before you cast out, it sinks like stone

Pete (the painter) Bond

Minepit Lake
Day Ticket – East Sussex

Address
See directions

Contact Details
Mr Ashley Groom
☎ 01892 665351 or
07545 064975

ashleygroom@me.com

www.thecarpsyndicate.co.uk

Nearest Main Town
Crowborough

Opening Hours
6.45am to dusk

Costs
Membership costs £50.
There will be a combined
membership of 50 members
split between the day ticket
lake and new Syndicate lake.
Memberships run from 1st
April and run for 12 months.

Day tickets cost:
£10 per day
£15 per 24 hours

Facilities

Carp Size

25lb+

The Fishery

Minepit Lake is a secure and picturesque water in the east of the county,
surrounded by woodlands and fields. It is a natural lake that was cleaned out
and extended in 2005 before being restocked with English fish. It is a private
day ticket water where membership is required.

Directions

Full directions are only given out when membership is taken.

The Lake

This 1½ acre, clay bottomed lake has lots of features including 2 islands, reed
beds and lily pads as well as underwater features to fish to. Depths range from
2 feet to nearly 15 feet. 6 swims are available and only 4 anglers are allowed a
one time.

Carp Stocks
Commons to 25lb+, mirrors to 25lb+. Total stock is unknown.

Fishery Rules

2 rods only. All sessions must be booked in advance. No one to arrive before
6.45am. Landing nets, weigh slings and unhooking mats are supplied for your
use, do not bring your own. Barbless hooks only. Safety rigs only. No braided
line except marker/spod rod. No particles except hemp seed are allowed,
strictly no nuts. No fixed leads, dogs, wading or swimming. All gates to be
closed behind you. All litter to be removed from the fishery. Kryston klin-ik or
similar to be used by all.

Additional Information

Disabled access. Stocked with young, fast growing and stunning looking fish. Other species include chub, perch, tench and barbel. A new 3½ acre lake was dug on site in late 2010 and will be opening in 2012 – see Syndicate section under Oaktree Lake, page 74.

Oast Farm Pond
Day Ticket – East Sussex

Address
TN22 4AU

Contact Details
Mr Philip Greenland
☎ 01825 733446

Nearest Main Town
Uckfield

Opening Hours
Dawn to dusk

Costs
Day tickets
Monday to Friday
All tickets cost £6
Weekend tickets cost £7 per day. No concessions.

The whole lake can be booked for £80

Facilities

Carp Size

27lb

The Fishery

A private water on farmland, set in a hollow and surrounded by trees, it originated over 100 years ago, but was de-silted and cleaned in 1983.

Directions

Take the A272 Buxted Road, which is 1 mile north east of Uckfield, and head towards the village of Buxted. At Coopers Green traffic lights look for the sign post for Oast Farm.

The Lake

An oval shaped, ½ acre water set on a peaceful countryside farm it has an inlet and outlet and plenty of bankside cover, including overhanging trees and bushes. Very little weed but some marginal reeds and willow trees. Depths up to nearly 6 feet and clay bottomed. No night fishing is allowed and 2 rods only. Contains a good few carp with upper double figure commons and mirrors to 27lb.

Fishery Rules

Barbless hooks only. No boilies allowed. Unhooking mats must be used. No dogs, carp sacks or litter. No bait boats.

Additional Information

Open all year. Not suitable for disabled anglers.

Other species include tench, roach, rudd and crucian carp.

Sundays are sometimes booked for matches.

A pod is for life, not just 'til Xmas.

Carp gear should be your faithful friend for life, and look 'the dog's…' That's why you've chosen **Solar Supreme Stainless** for almost 25 years. From its birth on Savay to the Worldwide's domination, Solar stands the test of time and all of the tests thrown at it. **Solar Supreme Stainless. Made in England. Always has been, always will be.**

Lockey *Helleur* *Briggs* *Gascoyne* *Crow*

New Website Coming Soon...
www.solartackle.co.uk
The tackle, the blogs, the info, the knowledge, the inside lane...

SOLAR TACKLE

...wide Pod owes ...ble ease-of-use, ...and stability to ...leg adjustment ...m. Look closely ...rldwide and you'll ...he world buys ...reme Stainless.

For the Sharper Carper.

From the iconic 'Sod' and 'Worldwide' pods, through our banksticks and buzzer bars to our fittings and indicators, you know that with Solar Supreme Stainless and Advanced Carbon you're making a long-term investment that will last you a lifetime.

* Worldwide Pod shown with Supreme Stainless 3 Rod Pozi-Loc Screwless Buzzer Bars, available separately.

Rowallen Fisheries
Day Ticket – East Sussex

Address
TN33 9JT

Contact Details
Chas Rowland
☎ 01424 223354
chas@rowallenfish.com

George Allen
☎ 07857 400645

www.rowallenfish.com

Nearest Main Town
Battle

Opening Hours
7am to 7pm

Costs
Adults, Juniors, OAP's and Disabled £7 for 2 rods

Membership – Adults £40
Concessions £30

Pay on the bank

Facilities

Carp Size

The Fishery

Rowallen Fisheries was set up in 1998 by George Allen and Chas Rowland, and both have been involved in lake management for almost 20 years. All the fish in these lakes have been home grown in their own stock lakes.

Directions

Situated in the village of Ninfield near Bexhill on Sea. Once in the village of Ninfield, on the A269, look for a large concrete water tower, Moorhall Drive is opposite the bus stop. Moorhall Lake is signposted.

The Lakes

The Old Lake

Formerly two lakes, which were joined together in 1998. 1½ acres in size this lake has depths which vary from 4 to 11 feet, with plenty of natural bankside cover. No weed present but a few lily pads.

Carp Stocks

Commons to 20lb+, mirrors to 20lb+.

Estimated Carp Stock – 200+ Fish.

The New Lake

Excavated in 2001 and 2½ acres in size, it has depths to 10 feet. Again, no weed but lily pads to fish to. In the summer of 2010 a few fish to over 20lb died, however, some bigger fish are still believed to be present.

Carp Stocks

Commons to 20lb+, mirrors to 20lb+.

Estimated Carp Stock – 200+ Fish.

Fishery Rules

Day fishing only. Barbless hooks only. 2 rods only. No carp sacks. No litter.
Fishing from swims only. No nut baits. No bait boats. Unhooking mats must be used. No rods to be left unattended. Under 16's must be accompanied by an adult.

Additional Information

These lakes have a close season from May 1st to June 15th. Other species include tench, roach, rudd and perch.

When fishing in amongst thick weed, braided line will cost you far less lost fish than nylon

Sam Rozier

Rye Nook Fishery
Day Ticket – East Sussex

Address
TN35 5JZ

Contact Details
Mr Peter Gould
☎ 01424 434464 or
07961 433701

admin@ryenookfishery.co.uk

www.ryenookfishery.co.uk

Nearest Main Town
Rye

Opening Hours
7am to 7pm

Costs
Day tickets are available from local tackle shops or from the shop in Oyster Creek Road, which is just outside the fishery entrance. They are also available on the bank but cost more.

Syndicate tickets £175–£320 (see lake descriptions)

Facilities

Carp Size

39lb

The Fishery

Based at Rye Harbour, in the east of the county, this fishery covers 100 acres of water created by gravel extraction between 1930 and 1970. Stocked in the mid 1950's, and originally run as a match and club venue for up to 300 anglers, the increasing interest in carp fishing has seen the establishment of both a carp syndicate and day tickets being available.

Directions

From Hastings take the A259 road to Rye. Just before the town of Rye you should look for Harbour Road, which is on the right. Travel down Harbour Road until you come to a church and housing estate, where the entrance to the fishery is on the right. If you reach the shops on the left you have just gone past the entrance.

The Lakes

Little Nook

A long thin boomerang shaped water of about 2 acres with depths between 7 to 8 feet. The lake is surrounded by reeds and overhanging trees and bushes. Only fishable from the harbour road side, it has 30 swims and night fishing is not allowed. Described as an ideal day ticket water for the leisure angler. With carp up to 12lb+, other species include roach, rudd, bream and perch.

Moorhen Lake

An oval shaped 2 acre pool that has 20 flat swims, this is a popular water which allows day only fishing. An open pool that holds mirrors and commons up to 25lb.

The Nook

A long meandering lake of 40 acres, with 100 plus swims, it has islands, reed beds and overhanging bushes. This water holds a lot of matches as it's stocked with roach, rudd, bream and carp. The carp are mostly commons that go up to just over 26lb. It also operates a night syndicate for up to 4 rods at £175 for all year round fishing. All the above waters have their own car parks.

The Ocean

50 acres of water and reserved for the syndicate members, it has 32 swims and depths that go between 7 to 9 feet. A relatively flat bottomed and featureless gravel pit that does get weedy in the summer months. Open all year and up to 4 rods allowed. 90% of the swims are accessible by car so disabled access is good. Commons in this lake go to just over 39lbs and mirrors go up to 38lb with a good number of back up fish and a lot of 20lbs. Syndicate membership is £320.

Fishery Rules

Barbless hooks only. Unhooking mats must be used. No dogs, boats or fires. Rods must not be left unattended.

Bait boats are not allowed.

NB: The Ocean allows the use of micro barbed hooks.

> You wouldn't eat the same food every day. A change of bait can sometimes be the difference between catching and a blank
>
> Clive Gibbons

Southbourne Lake
Day Ticket – East Sussex

Address
BN23 6QJ

Contact Details
☎ 01323 520229
www.emsr.co.uk

Nearest Main Town
Eastbourne

Opening Hours
2nd April 8am to 5pm.
1st May to 18th September
9am to 9pm.
19th September to
30th October 8am to 5pm.

Costs
Membership fee is £65 for
all members.

Daily prices are as follows:

April and 19th September to
30th October – £8
OAP £6

May to 18th September
– £12
OAP £8

Facilities

Carp Size

31lb

E .M .S .R. (Eastbourne Miniature Steam Railway)

The Fishery

This is a private, members only day ticket water in the grounds of the
Eastbourne Miniature Steam Railway Park. Memberships are limited to a small
number.

Directions

A short distance from the sea in the Roselands area of Eastbourne. Heading
into Eastbourne on the A22 you will come to Lottbridge Drove. The entrance
is on the right, just past the roundabout, and signposted (brown sign) "Mini
Railway".

The Lake

This figure of eight shaped lake of 5 acres was man made in 1986 by East
Sussex County Council. It has 23 swims, covering over half of the bank,
available for fishing. The south bank is not accessible to the public, including
anglers, as this area is set aside as a conservation area and has been extensively
planted with trees and bushes, giving plenty of cover for the fish within a
castable area. The lake is weed free apart from a few marginal reeds and the
depths vary from 9 to 6 feet. The west side of the lake is the shallower side
of the water, with a shelving shore. There is an island on the fishable side and
an inlet from the small Lottbridge River which runs past the fishery. Species
include bream, roach, perch and a few rudd and tench. It is stocked extensively
with both large and small mirrors which go to almost 31lb and also contains a
few commons to 18lb+. Water holds a lot of mirrors.

Fishery Rules

Barbless hooks only. 3 rods allowed. Night fishing is not allowed and times vary throughout the year(see legend). No carp sacks. Unhooking mats must be used and rods must not be left unattended. Fishing in designated swims only. This water is only open from 2nd April until 30th October each year. No dogs or litter.

Additional Information.

Members may take up to 5 guests per season for the day ticket price. Swims can be pre-booked up to 14 days in advance. Litter bins provided. This is an adults only fishery.

In winter fill your kettle before you go to sleep, now't more annoying than a frozen water bottle in the morning

Mike Brown

Swanborough Farm
Day Ticket – East Sussex

Address
Nr. Lewes

Contact Details
Mr Greenwood
☎ 01273 477388 or
07850 811704

www.swanboroughfarm.co.uk

Nearest Main Town
Lewes

Opening Hours
7am – 7pm

Costs
Adult day ticket £10
Half day £5
Overnight ticket £15
24 hours £20
Juniors (under16) £5 per day

All above prices are based on 2 rods. Third rod at extra cost (speak to the bailiff at the lake).

All overnight & 24 hour sessions must be booked and you must arrive before the gates close.

Facilities

Carp Size

The Fishery

Swanborough is a 1000 acre farm set in the heart of the east of the county. The farm sits at the picturesque foot of the South Downs, south of Lewes. It has been owned by the Greenwood family for the past 100 years and the fishery has been established for over 8 years.

Directions

Driving east on the A27 towards Lewes from Brighton, proceed past the Falmer University site and the new Brighton football stadium until you come to a large roundabout, take the third exit signposted to Kingston. Follow this road for about ½ a mile through the village of Kingston until you come to a T-junction. Turn right and after about 600 yards you should spot the fishery signpost on your left. Follow the track to the car park.

The Lakes

There are three lakes at Swanborough. The first two are smaller lakes and do not stock carp. The Carp Lake (as it's called) is the biggest at 3½ acres, then there's Tench and Decoy Lakes.

Carp Lake

This quite open 3½ acre lake has 18 flat grassy swims and depths that start at 4 feet to a maximum of 12 feet. There is no weed but it is ringed with reeds and a few lily pads. Described as an easy water with outstanding views.

Carp Stocks
Commons to 27lb, mirrors to 30lb+.

Estimated total stock – 100+ fish.

Tench Lake
A 2 acre lake with 15 swims holding tench, bream, perch, roach and rudd.

Decoy Lake
This 1½ acre lake has 12 swims and has chubb, perch, roach and rudd.

Fishery Rules
Barbless or micro barbed hooks only. No nuts, dogs, litter or fires. Unhooking mats must be used. All anglers must carry Kryston klin-ik. Bait boats are allowed.

Small groups of water birds grubbing about on the surface are sometimes a good sign that carp are present in the area

Kevin Peet

Tanyard Fisheries
Day Ticket – East Sussex

Address
TN22 3RL

Contact Details
Mr Steve Boreham
☎ 01825 791010 or
07833 532842

www.tanyardfisheries.co.uk

Nearest Main Town
Uckfield

Opening Hours
Day ticket 7am to 7pm
Night ticket 5pm to 7pm the
following day

Costs
Day tickets
1 rod £9, 2 rods £12
3 rods £15

Night tickets
2 rods £18, 3 rods £24

All tickets finish at 7pm on
your last day.

Facilities

Car parking at all lakes.
Washing up room.

Carp Size

The Fishery

This is a 7 lake complex set on the edge of the Sheffield Forest in the
east of the county. First constructed in 1987 by the owner, Bernie Brown,
they have matured into beautiful rich waters that are home to specimen
sized fish of all species. The grounds of this fishery are treated as a
garden and the lakes have all been planted with water plants to give an
aesthetically pleasing look.

Directions

Heading south on the A22 go through East Grinstead and Forest Row
until you come to Wych Cross. Look for the Roebuck Hotel, just past the
lights, and turn right onto the A275 towards Lewes. Follow this road for
3 miles and go through the village of Danehill. Keep on the A275 for a
further 1 mile and you will see Heaven Farm Caravan Park on the right.
Take the second left past the farm, which is Tanyard Lane and the venue is
½ mile on the right.

The Lakes

Coarse Pool 1

This is the smallest water on the complex at ½ an acre. This lake is to be
stocked with carp to 8lb sometime in 2010/2011.

Coarse Pools 2 and 3

Both these pools are similar in size and stock levels. 1 acre with depths to
4½ feet. They have overhanging alder trees and beds of rushes and irises.

Carp stocks

Both waters hold a lot of fish in the 6lb to 15lb range. Pool 2 has produced fish to 21lb+ and Pool 3 fish to 23lb+. There are also a good head of Koi present.

Pool 4 is a carp free lake.

Specimen Lake 1

This 2 acre lake has an island and small leaf lily along the margins as well as overhanging willows, rushes and a woodland side. An ideal stalking water. Depths go down to 6½ feet .

Carp stocks

Commons and mirrors to 31lb+. 19 different 20lb+ fish and a 31lb+ fully scaled mirror.

Estimated total stock – 100 plus fish.

Specimen Lake 2

This lake is an acre in size and described as an intimate water, with only 5 swims which all have their own area of water. Contains 2 islands and large lily beds with depths down to 6½ feet.

Carp stocks

Home to 6 30lb+ to 38lb+ carp. Also 22 fish over 20lb and only a few doubles.

Estimated total stock – 50+ fish.

Specimen Lake 3

The largest on the complex at 3 acres, this 6½ feet deep, clay bottomed lake has large beds of rises around the margins and big beds of rushes and reeds. Overhanging alders separate the swims.

Carp stocks

3 30lb+ to 34lb fish and 17 over 20lb+. Also a range of commons and mirrors over 10lb+.

Estimated total stock – 130+ fish.

Fishery Rules.

No barbed hooks. No fixed leads. Minimum 10lb breaking strain line. No rod sharing or unattended rods and no nut baits of any kind. No carp sacks but unhooking mats are compulsory. No overnight guests. No dogs.

Additional Info

Very secure fenced fishery with locked gates. Well maintained and extremely tidy swims and walkways to each lake. Litter is not tolerated. Fishery has own aquarium. Specimen Lake 3 holds some very big cats to over 60lb. No booking, just turn up and fish.

Weir Wood Reservoir
Day Ticket – East Sussex

Address
RH18 5HT

Contact Details
Mike Smith
☎ 01342 820650

www.weirwoodangling.co.uk

enquiries@weirwoodangling.
co.uk

Nearest Main Town
East Grinstead

Opening Hours
Day ticket 7.30am-5.30pm
Evening ticket 4.30pm-9.30pm
Night ticket 5pm to 7pm the
following day

Costs
Days only
Adults £10 for 2 rods,
3rd rod £5 extra
Juniors £5 for 2 rods only
(under 12 fish free with
paying adult).

Evening ticket
£8 for 2 rods, 3rd rod £3
extra

Night fishing £15 for 3 rods.
24 hours £20 for 3 rods.

48 hours £35 for 3 rods

Companions welcome but
must not fish unless they
purchase a relevant ticket.

Facilities

Carp Size

30lb+

The Fishery

Weirwood Reservoir is the counties second biggest stillwater. The biggest by
far is Bewl Water, which covers 780 acres but, unfortunately for the carp angler,
coarse fishing on this giant of a water is not permitted (although carp do
exist). Weirwood covers 280 acres and is 1½ miles long. Built over the period
1951 to 1954 by damming the valley of the River Medway, it supplies water
for many local towns. Sitting in stunning Weald surroundings near the village of
Forest Row, the reservoir caters for a whole host of activities including sailing,
canoeing and angling. The angling on offer is trout and pike fishing and general
coarse fishing on a day ticket basis, however there is also a small carp syndicate
(see Syndicate section on page 80).

Directions

From East Grinstead going south on the A22 go past the village of Ashurst
Wood until you come to Forest Row. As you enter Forest Row you will
come to a mini roundabout, take the right turn which is Priory Road and the
entrance to the Reservoir is signposted on the right, a couple of hundred yards
along Priory Road. Follow the lane and signs to the car park.

The Water

Of the 280 acres of water, 250 acres are fishable with the rest set aside as
an SSSI site and nature reserve. Day ticket anglers have the use of 50% of
the Reservoir from the dam wall and along the north bank. Depths fluctuate
throughout the year but when full the maximum depth is 39 feet. The deepest
area is where the old river runs through, but areas of 6 to 8 feet can be found

along the south bank, although the average depth is 14 to 15 feet. The lake bed is sandstone, weed free and relativity flat. The water holds vast numbers of fish, including big roach and bream, pike, trout and a small number of tench.

The head of carp is unknown but fish to mid-thirties have been landed. A good number of 20lb+ fish are present and it would be no surprise if it threw up something special.

Fishery Rules

3 rods are allowed. No carp sacks. Unhooking mats must be used. No fires, dogs, litter or bar-b-ques. Lead core is banned. Bait boats are allowed. Night fishing is now allowed on a day ticket.

Additional Information

Weirwood Reservoir operates a close season and the water closes on February 28th and re-opens on June 16th.

Wylands International Angling Centre
Day Ticket – East Sussex

Address

TN33 0SU

Contact Details

☎ 01424 893394

info@wylands.co.uk

www.wylands.co.uk

For up to date info call the bailiff, Neil Ager, on
☎ 07722 882993

Nearest Main Town

Battle

Opening Hours

Day – 7am to 7pm

Nights – 7pm to 7am

24 hrs – from point of arrival

Costs

24 hour day ticket:

Adults £12

OAP's £10

Junior (12 to 16) £10

Junior (under 12) £5

Prices are for 2 rods. Extra rods charged at £6 per day

Weekly ticket £70

Season ticket £200

Facilities

Carp Size

34lb+

The Fishery

Wylands is one of the biggest angling centres in the UK. Situated in the east of the county, near Battle, 1066 country, the complex is home to ten lakes that cater for all types of anglers, from the pleasure and match angler to the serious carper this venue has something for all, including some big carp.

Directions

From the town of Hastings head north on the A21. Look for Battle Road on the left – the B2159. Stay on this road for about 1½ miles and turn left at the roundabout onto the A2100, this is still Battle Road. Carry on for another 1¼ miles up Battle Hill, still on the A2100. When you go over a railway line look for Powdermill Lane, which is on the left, this is the B2095. Go past Powdermills Hotel on your right and the complex entrance is on the left, look for signpost.

The Lakes

House Lake (1)

This 2½ acre water has 3 small islands and depths that reach 10 feet. It's close to all the fishery facilities and can get busy in the summer months. Mirrors go to over 24lb and commons to 29lb+. Also holds bream and large tench. Total carp stock is estimated in the hundreds.

Lakes 2, 3 and 4, Junior, Rosie's and Snake Match

These waters are rated as 'easy'. Junior, as the name suggests, is for those anglers just starting out. Rosie's is suitable for disabled anglers and Snake Match is over 2 miles long and split into three match lakes with 205 pegs. All hold a good head of tench, roach, perch, chub, bream, rudd and crucian carp.

Field Lake (5)

This 1½ acre lake is described as the ideal place to start fishing for the youngster. Has depths to 6 feet, is weed free and is stocked with lots of smaller carp. Does hold commons to 23lb+ and some good sized mirrors. A good floater water. Also holds plenty of tench.

Middle Lake (6)

Arguably the best all round water on the complex. Fishes well in all seasons. 2½ acres in size, with a depth up to 6 feet, it has produced mirrors to over 22lb and commons to just short of 27lb. Total carp stock is in the hundreds. Other species include bream, tench and perch.

Kell Lake (7)

Described as one of the more difficult waters to fish, this 2½ acre water has depths that vary from 6 to 8 feet. Does produce the most doubles on the complex, with mirrors going to 34lb+ and commons to almost 32lb. Total carp stock is unknown but holds at least 50 doubles.

Maisie's Lake (8)

3 acres of open water and rated as easy. Only recently opened and stocked with roach, rudd, bream, perch, tench and mirrors and commons that go to over 12lb. A runs water.

Old Specimen Lake (9)

A 2½ acre lake that has two islands and depths that go down to 8 feet. Described as a moderate water, it holds lots of small carp but has produced both commons and mirrors to over 20lb. Other species include tench, roach and rudd.

New Specimen Lake (10)

This 2½ acre lake has depths to just over 8 feet. Probably the longest walk from the centres facilities and described as sometimes difficult. Has a large central island and some big commons to over 33lb and mirrors to 28lb+. Contains a large stock of doubles and upper doubles. Total carp stock is in the hundreds and is also home to big barbel and roach.

All the waters on this complex are weed and pike free and the bottom is clay.

Fishery Rules

Barbless hooks only. No sacks. No fish lifted above the knee! No bait boats. No unattended tackle. No swimming, radios or fires. Unhooking mats must be used.

Other general rules apply

Bait Bans The following are not permitted for use – Nuts, peas, beans, bloodworm, joker. Trout or pond pellets, fishmeal based boilies or groundbait or trout pellet groundbait.

Additional Information

All landing nets and weigh slings must be dipped in tubs provided. Open all year.

Dogs on a lead are allowed.

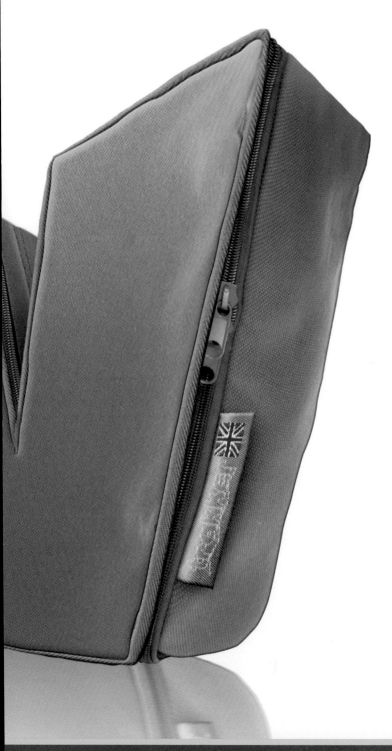

trakker
One step ahead.

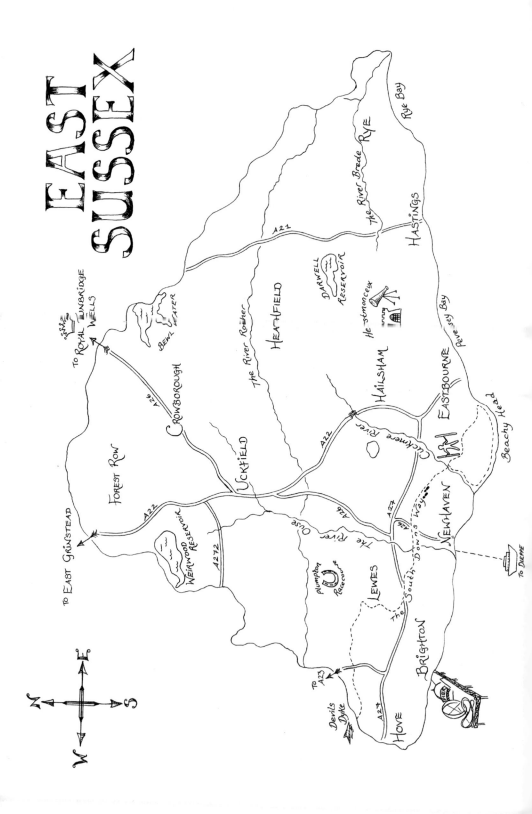

Contents

Clive Vale Angling Club
Club Waters – East Sussex

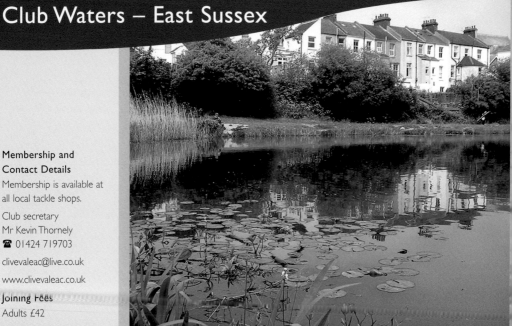

Membership and Contact Details

Membership is available at all local tackle shops.

Club secretary
Mr Kevin Thornely
☎ 01424 719703

clivevaleac@live.co.uk

www.clivevaleac.co.uk

Joining Fees

Adults £42

OAP/Disabled £28

Junior Under 15 Years £24

Carp Size

30lb

Club History/Introduction

Founded in Hastings by a local fisherman in 1912, the club is open to all anglers from beginners to specimen hunters and matchmen. The club, which is run by its members, has stillwaters and stretches of river to fish in the east of the county and has a variety of fisheries.

Waters

Clive Vale Reservoir (Hastings)

A mixed fishery that has been established for over 100 years, comprising of 2 small lakes divided by a gravel track. The big reservoir is around an acre in size, the smaller about ¾ of an acre. The bigger lake has depths down to 9 feet whilst the smaller is shallower with a maximum depth of 4 feet. Both waters have weed and lily pads and a clay/silty bottom. 16+ swims on big lake and 12+ on small lake. Both are open all year and the club offers day tickets which can be purchased from the bailiff on the bank. No night fishing is allowed. 2 rods only. Commons and mirrors to 15lb+. Other species include roach, rudd, tench, bream, perch and crucians to 2lbs. Barbless hooks only at this venue.

The Beeches (Wittersham)

A small, kidney shaped lake of an acre which is owned by the club. It has depths of up to 8 feet and is prone to be heavily weeded in the summer months. Stocked with tench, roach, rudd and carp which have all bred successfully. Lots of commons into double figures and mirrors up to 19lb. Night fishing is allowed and the lake is open all year. Also present are perch and large eels.

Saunders Gravel Pit (Rye Harbour)

An extensive former gravel works with 25 plus acres of water. Limited to 30 anglers a day, juniors are not allowed at this venue unless accompanied by an adult. An interestingly shaped water with many bays and arms and varying depths down to 12 feet. No weed, but has a few lily pads, bars and plateaux. Set in open countryside with little bankside cover and steep banks. Lots of commons of all sizes up to almost 30lb. A good number of 20lb+ fish and a few mirrors to mid double figures. Has an out of bounds area called the Islands. This water has a traditional close season and night fishing is not allowed. Other fish present are bream, tench, roach, rudd, perch and some large eels.

Pannel Lane (Pett)

Secured by the club in 2009, this is an irrigation lake of just over an acre in size. It was once a carp stock pond and it's not known what fish might have escaped the nets before the club took control. Up to 14 feet deep and clay bottomed. Only 10 anglers a day are allowed and these must be booked in advance. Night fishing is allowed. 2 rods only. Lots of mirrors and commons up to 10lb+ and also known to hold some rudd.

Point Field Pit (Camber)

A gravel pit of 3 acres, with depths down to 12 feet, but with no weed. Secured by the club in June 2010, so fish stocks are unknown. An open water that has cover on just one bank, there are 20 swims and off road parking. Commons to 25lb+ and mirrors to 26lb+, with some heavily plated mirrors to 17lb+. Rudd and eels also present. Night fishing is allowed. 2 rods only.

Club Rivers.

Clive Vale members can also fish for carp on the Royal Military Canal and the Rivers Rother (eastern) and Brede. See River section for more details on pages 208 to 213.

Cranbrook & District Angling Club
Club Waters – East Sussex

Membership and Contact Details

Membership runs from 1st June to 31st May each year.

Forms can be downloaded at www.cranbrookanglingclub.co.uk

Membership secretary – Mr Mark Lindsell,
☎ 07973 383952

membership@cranbrookanglingclub.co.uk

Joining Fees

Adults £63 + £10 work party levy

Juniors under 16 – £28

Intermediates (16 to 18 years) & OAP's (65+) £36

Boat permits (with key) for Darwell Reservoir £20

Work party levy will be credited towards membership subscription upon renewal the following year. Levy does not apply to OAP's, disabled, junior or intermediate members.

Members' guest tickets are available at £6 per day.

Carp Size

20lb+

Club History/Introduction

Although Cranbrook and District is an angling club based in the county of Kent, they do have 2 venues in Sussex. Formed in 1951, this growing club has over 500 members and a wide variety of waters for all types of fishing, which is open to all. Members come from as far as Devon and Yorkshire, and it is a members-only club with no day tickets available.

Darwell Reservoir

An unknown quantity – that's some statement for a water that covers 156 acres and is just over a mile long. Set in the most dramatic and unspoilt Sussex countryside, with an abundance of wildlife roaming its banks, including deer and wild boar, this large expanse of water is very under fished, especially by carp anglers, so the numbers and sizes of the carp are still a mystery. Rumours of sightings of large fish have been reported to the club, but none have ever been landed. It is known that a vast number of the carp present are commons, with very few mirrors ever reported.

The water levels can change quite dramatically, as the reservoir is used by Southern Water customers living in the Hastings area, but it has depths of up to 40 feet when full. The west end of the water is the shallowest area, with depths no more than 6 feet.

Club members can fish the ¼ mile long dam wall and 300 yards of the northern bank, the rest of the reservoir can only be fished by boat. These are controlled by the club and must be booked in advance. Known to hold some trout from its fly fishing days, it is also home to some large pike, perch and eels plus shoals of roach and dace and some tench, bream and chub. The biggest common reported was some years ago at just over 24lb, plenty of double figure fish have been landed with the odd 20lb plus fish, but it would be no surprise if a large common was caught.

The banks have plenty of cover with overhanging trees and bushes. Night fishing is not allowed and the reservoir is patrolled 24 hours a day. Access is strictly dawn to dusk and 3 rods may be used. Onsite facilities include a toilet and car park. This reservoir has very strict rules, and members found ignoring them will be caught and banned. A water for the pioneering angler!

Springwood Fishery

This is a mature, 4 water fishery, formed around 25 years ago and set in a hillside, it is located in quiet surroundings on the border of Kent, near the village of Flimwell. Night fishing is allowed on Spring Pool and Beech Pool only. This venue has the benefit of onsite car parking and toilet and shower facilities, next to the fishing lodge. These lakes are 2 rods only with a maximum stay of 48 hours on Spring and Beech pools.

Spring Pool

The biggest lake on the venue at 3 acres and with depths down to 14 feet, it has a shallow bay, an island and 20 swims with plenty of bankside cover. No weed. It has produced commons and mirrors to mid 20lb and grass carp to upper 20lb. Other species include tench, perch, roach and massive catfish .

Beech Pool

An intimate ½ an acre pool with no weed. Home to catfish, tench, roach and a few carp into double figures, plus some Koi carp. Rules as Spring Pool.

Match Lake

12 platformed swims on ½ an acre of water. Depths of 6 to 7 feet and weed free. Lots of commons and mirrors to 10lb plus lots of silver fish. No night fishing allowed.

Top Pool

A small ½ an acre pool described as the ideal water for juniors and disabled anglers. No weed, and depths up to 4 feet. Holds bream, tench, roach, common, mirror and crucian carp. Easy access from the car park. No night fishing allowed.

Crowborough & District Anglers Association
Club Waters – East Sussex

Membership and Contact Details

Join online at
www.cdaa.btinternet.co.uk

Postal applications to
The Treasurer.
Mrs Sandra Lawrence
Sorrento
Western Road
Crowborough
East Sussex
TN6 3ES

Club secretary
Geoff Wicks
☎ 01892 655935

Joining Fees

Adults £45
Husband & wife £65
OAP's/Disabled/Student £33
Junior £19

+ £5 joining fee for new
members, apart from Juniors
who have no joining fee.

Carp Size

20lb+

Club History/Introduction

C.D.A.A was founded in 1948 and claims to be one of the first angling clubs to obtain lottery funding to create a new venue, which includes facilities for the disabled angler. Apart from the stillwaters, it also controls 14 miles of the River Rother, and has just recently secured fishing rights to part of Weir Wood Reservoir (see Day Ticket section on page 44 for details of Weir Wood).

It has a book exchange with four other clubs in East and West Sussex which gives members access to a further 12 lakes and 16 rivers and drains.

The Waters

Shannons Old Lake

A small water of just over ½ acre which has 12 platform swims. Depths vary between 3 to 4 feet, with lily pads and weed beds. The lake is home to double figure commons and mirrors. Other species include tench, roach, rudd, perch and chub. On site car parking and no close season on this water.

Underhill Lake

A 1 acre water which is only open from dawn to dusk, Wednesday to Sunday inclusive. A mixed fishery that holds only small carp to about 9lb.

Waldron Lake

An attractive small lake of just under an acre. Weed free and holding ghost, grass and common carp to 15lb.

Scaland Wood

Night fishing is allowed on this popular, ¾ acre venue which has depths between 5 to 10 feet. A mixed fishery that has both commons and mirrors to 12lb+. Night fishing is limited to 4 anglers only. No close season on this water.

Wirgol

Near the town of Crowborough, these 2 ponds are ½ an acre each. Depths range from 3 to 6 feet and the lake is weed free. Holds mirrors and commons to 20lb+. 2 rods on all waters. Onsite parking. Night fishing is not allowed.

Club Rivers

Sections of River Rother and Royal Military Canal. For details see pages 208 and 213 in the River section.

Stick with 2 or 3 rigs you are happy with, results will be more consistent if you don't keep changing rigs

Steve Briggs

Dorset Arms Angling Club
Club Waters – East Sussex

Membership and Contact Details

The club's season runs from 1st May to 1st March. One stillwater is kept open all year, which changes from time to time.

Membership online at www.dorsetarmsangling.co.uk

Postal address:
Mr M Simmons Laundry Cottage, Whiligh, Wadhurst, East Sussex, TN5 7JU

☎ 01892 785520 or 07902 216852

E mail info@ dorsetarmsangling.co.uk

Joining Fees

Adult £42
Family ticket £45
OAP/disabled £15

New members £5 joining fee

Juniors £12 + £2 new members joining fee.

Carp Size

17lb+

Club History/Introduction

This small club was established in1959 in the Dorset Arms pub, in the village of Withyham, hence the name. Membership is open to all and this friendly club offers both river and stillwater fishing and has about 80 members.

Club Waters

Burrswood Estate Bottom Lake

This 1½ acre water is set in the grounds of the beautiful Burrswood Estate and is surrounded by peaceful woodland. It has a hard clay bottom and depths going to 4 feet, with sets of lily pads and some weed beds. A good head of commons and mirrors to 17lb+ have been landed but it's thought that bigger fish are present. 2 rods only. No night fishing. Other species present are bream, roach, perch and crucian carp. It has 26 swims.

Burrswood Top Lake

This is the smaller lake at the top of the estate and has pleasant views of the Sussex countryside. It has a hard stone bottom and is, in places, dense with lily pads in the summer. Carp sizes are unknown but doubles are said to be present. Both lakes are under fished. 2 rods only. No night fishing.

Club shares Shannon's Old Lake with Crowborough and District. Details in CDAA section on page 56.

River and Canal

Controls stretches of the Rother and Royal Military Canal – see pages 208 and 213 in River section.

Winter Edges

by Clive Williams

Although my own time spent on the bank actually fishing in the winter is now very restricted, I have, over the seasons done my fair share of wishing I was at times somewhere else. I know plenty of anglers who spend the whole calendar year in pursuit of carp, no matter what the conditions and occasionally winter dreams do come true.

Clothing

Some of the little edges that can be done to help the angler feel more comfortable on the bank are just as important as any good winter bait. If you are dry and warm you are less likely to curl up in the bag and roll the bivvy door down, missing any possible signs of activity in your swim. A good winter suit is a must but remember to wear 2 or 3 layers underneath any such suit. The first layer should be designed to be worn next to the skin so it needs to be made from materials such as polyester or merino wool. This ensures the wearer stays perspiration free, which is the first step to feeling warm and comfortable, and ideally these garments should be of the underwear type with a crewneck top and long johns.

The next layer should be good fitting garment/s that do not hinder or restrict your movements. Again polyester types are the best and many tackle companies produce excellent two-piece under-suits that fit this bill perfectly, Trakker Products producing one of the best. You now have the ideal layers to both sleep in and wear under your final layer of clothing.

The wind and its chill factor are one of the things that make for very uncomfortable fishing and an early return home, so when choosing the outer layer take into consideration the type of water you fish. If you tend to fish windy, open waters any item of clothing made with an outer skin of Pertex would be ideal. Pertex is a brilliant lightweight fabric, originally designed for people (nutters) who climb mountains. This is a highly breathable fabric that is totally windproof. The down side of Pertex is that although it is water resistant it is not 100% waterproof so some kind of water resistant shell would be needed in case of rain. If the extra waterproof garment is something you don't want to carry, then simply choose any of the top quality two-piece suits available today that are waterproof. My own personal choice for any winter trips I might do are a bit of a mix and match. I wear the two first layers already mentioned, my trousers are Trakker's Delta range; these are hard wearing and thermal lined and they are also breathable and waterproof, with pockets and a zipped fly. The hydrostatic head of this material is 3,000mm (waterproof). My jacket is made of Pertex. I always carry (summer and winter) a roll up, small lightweight waterproof downpour jacket which I can quickly slip on if needed. I tend to like my outer shells a size bigger as I find this more comfortable. A good hat is essential to slow down your body's heat loss.

A good pair of boots are also essential, warm and waterproof being the main requrement. If you like to wear the Skee-tex type of thermal and waterproof boots take a small saucepan with you. You can then boil lake water all day long and tip it onto your boots, thus keeping your feet as warm as toast.

A few of the lads on the syndicate I fish have got into using throw away bar-b-ques this winter. This gives a nice glow just inside the bivvy door whilst cooking a few sausages. Finally, when you do climb into the bag, don't forget the hot water bottle.

Single Hookbaits

A cold water tactic that has, over the years, put many a good carp on the bank is the single hookbait. Fished all alone and in some cases in the middle of nowhere it's surprising just how easy the carp can find them. I have always liked fishing over bait, even in the winter, however I have caught a few carp fishing singles myself, so it is something always worth a try. Most anglers use a pop-up boilie when single bait fishing but on the busier waters it may well pay off to do something a bit different and use a bottom bait in the same manner, especially if fishing on clean, weed free lake beds. Single hookbaits can be glugged and over-flavoured, giving off a greater pulling power and they can also be very bright fluoro colours for visual attraction.

Try casting a single bait out every hour or so to different spots and you may just cast one near an interested carp.

Gin Clear Water

At times carp anglers, myself included, are guilty of giving the carp far more intelligence than they clearly have, however when waters go gin clear in winter, our end tackle is very visible to the carp so anything that can be done to disguise and conceal the rig has to be a good thing, if only for the state of your own mind. Flying back leads have to play a part if this is how you need to go and there are a few good ones available today.

One of the most effective changes that can be made is to switch to a fluorocarbon hooklink. Fluorocarbon is virtually invisible in water and is easy to knot but as it is quite a stiffish line, to prevent the possibility of a loop forming when cast out, add a blob of Kryston putty or a Korda sinker to make sure the rig is flat on the lake bed. Lead core can play a part in the disguise of our rigs, but personally I don't think it's necessary with the excellent products available to us all today. Lead core can be a very dangerous product if not used in the correct manner so if you are unsure do not use it. Both Korda and Kryston, amongst others, produce a fantastic range of fluorocarbon hooklink material from 5lb up to 24lb.

The Mobile Approach

Location is, without question, one of the most important aspects of any winter trip. Carp on many waters are quite happy to find a winter spot they are comfortable to stay in and never move unless disturbed. This can be shallow or deep water so keeping an eye on all the known spots is worth bearing in mind. If you see any signs of carp, whether it be a clear sighting or just a maybe, move straightaway. Casting to showing fish is often known to produce a fish or two, so be mobile if you can.

General Tips

Maggots can be a brilliant winter bait if your chosen venue is not stacked with loads of silver fish. Fish them on a Korda maggot clip and cast a small PVA bag full to the spot, recasting at least every two hours.

If you can get away with it, scale all your rigs down in size and hit even the slightest twitch or single bleep of the buzzer.

Unless you can bait up with extreme accuracy, keep bait to a minimum.

Fish stringers or PVA bags.

I would have no problem baiting a margin spot with a big handful of hemp if I could cast my rig right on top of it.

Do not spread bait out, make the carp want the only mouthful available, the one with your rig in it.

Choose a water with a high stock level and one that gets fished a lot. Waters like my syndicate that get left alone in winter have a tendency to shut up shop and the carp lie dormant for weeks on end.

Shallower waters tend to fish better during the colder months, and carp get caught in three feet of water, beneath the ice, more times than you would believe.

Always watch and copy what the successful anglers on the lake do, there is no shame in learning from others.

Hastings & District Freshwater Angling Association Club Waters – East Sussex

Membership and Contact Details

The Club's season runs from 1st April to 31st March each year.

Membership application forms can be downloaded from www.hastingsandbexhillangling.co.uk

Club Secretary
Mr Alan Carter
☎ 01424 223234

Write to: 156 Ninfield Road, Bexhill on Sea, East Sussex, TN39 5BD (include a stamped address envelope)

E-mail info@hastingsandbexhillangling.co.uk

Joining Fees

Adult – £45

OAP, Disabled, Ladies, Junior (under 16) £25

Winter ticket from 1st October available at
£25 Adult
£15 Junior

Carp Size

35lb

Club History/Introduction

Established in 1895, this association provides fishing on various lakes and rivers, including some day ticket waters. Currently it has five lakes which hold a mixture of species, with the carp topping 35lb. In recent years they have introduced some young, fast growing carp into their waters and are continually looking to improve what is on offer to their members.

The Waters

Normanhurst Lake

This is a stunning 3 acre estate lake near Catsfield, which is surrounded by trees and set in peaceful countryside. It contains mirrors and commons to over 20lb and over the last few years several introductions of young fish have supplemented the well established stocks. The lake is fishable to club members only and night fishing between the hours of 10pm to 4am is not permitted. 2 rods only. Most of the carp stocks range from 15lb to 19lb and other species include rudd, tench, perch and crucians.

Broomham Pond

Two small ponds on the same Normanhurst Estate. Again these can only be fished by association members. Both waters hold carp to 17lb+, and are described as an ideal place for the pleasure angler with the chance of catching some nice doubles. 2 rods only. Does also hold some big tench, along with other species.

Buckshole Reservoir

Day tickets and night fishing are both available on this 3½ acre water that has seen a number of stockings of good young fish since 2000, the last in February of 2010 when a few mid doubles were introduced. The water contains two known thirties to 35lb+ and in excess of twenty 20lb+ fish. Also present are pike, roach, rudd, bream and perch. Night fishing for members costs £2 per night. Disabled swim available. 2 rods only, however, 3 rods can be used with prior permission.

Wishing Tree Reservoir

This 4 acre water holds hundreds of carp and is rated as very easy. Depths vary from 2 to 5 feet, at the dam end, and night fishing is allowed to members and day ticket holders. Although the majority of the carp are commons from 3lb to 10lb, a number of doubles are present along with a few elusive 20lb+ mirrors. Floaters work well in the summer. 2 rods only.

Harmers Pond

Situated in the 100 plus acre Alexander Park in Hastings, this ½ acre pond holds some good carp amongst the tench and silver fish that are present. Mid double figure mirrors and commons to over 23lb have been caught on boilies. Nights are allowed but tickets must be purchased in advance. 2 rods only. Good disabled access. There are toilets and a cafe in the park.

Club Rivers

Details of two stretches of water – the River Rother and Wallers Haven – can be found on pages 208 and 214 in the River section.

Seaford Angling Club
Club Waters – East Sussex

Membership and Contact Details

Download membership form at www.seafordanglingclub.co.uk

Postal address:
PO Box 168, Newhaven, Sussex BN9 1AW

☎ 07789 541677

sec@seafordanglingclub.co.uk

Memberships run from 1st April to 31st March.

Joining Fees

Entrance fee for new members £15

Adults – £40

Juniors (under 16)/OAP's & Disabled – £25

Family ticket (2 adult 2 junior) – £100

Non fishing member £5

Carp Size

Club History/Introduction

Seaford Angling Club was formed in the late 1950's to cater for all types of freshwater fishing in the local area and is based in the town of Seaford.

Club Waters

Michelham Priory

This 7 acre water is a moat which surrounds the Priory and is set in very peaceful grounds. It is a shallow, silty water with only 8 swims, and has some lily pads and bankside cover. Mirrors and commons go to low 20lbs. 2 rods only and no night fishing. Other species include pike, tench and roach. Onsite parking. This water has a close season.

Piddinghoe Pond

A barren, open water of 12 acres and 22 swims, this is a flat bottomed sand pit with an average depth of 5 feet and no weed. This water is open all year and holds carp to over 20lb. 2 rods only. Night fishing is allowed. Other species include roach, rudd, bream and perch.

The Old River

This water was once part of the River Ouse before being transformed into what is today a fully enclosed stillwater. It is described as a family, mixed fishery with depths going to 5 feet. Stocked with roach, rudd, tench, bream, pike and perch it also holds quite a good stock of double figure carp and commons that go to 25lb+. Open all year. 2 rods only. Night fishing is allowed.

Club Rivers and Drain

Controls stretches of the Rivers Ouse and Cuckmere plus Wallers Haven drain. See page 206 in the Rivers section and page 214 in the Miscellaneous Drain section.

It looks a bit Fred Carno's but this is the rig as I fish it successfully at the pressured, 'riggy' Birch Grove, using 8mm baits and a trimmed cork ball.

'm not a fan of pop-up rigs but I do accept that there are times when I really want to draw attention to the hookbait. There are some times of the year, and some sessions, when you just don't know how strongly they are feeding and you have to try and trigger a response. Over the years I have done a great deal of winter carping and during one particularly frustrating winter on Birch Grove – a very 'riggy' water – I started playing around with Albert Romp's concept of multiple hookbaits. Albert starting fishing multiples on Savay when he felt that the carp were conditioned to finding stringers, and his 'stringer hookbait' provided an element of surprise. His idea was very successful. Well, I've had some success on Albert's concept but during the winter in question I took it a stage further and combined the multiple concept with the pop-up/snowman idea, fishing the multiple hookbait vertically rather than horizontally – I guess it's an extension of the multiple, the snowman and the pop-up rigs!

must have been feeling brave to put this rig out at Birch but it was one of those 'nothing to lose' periods, and the set-up really came up trumps! In advance I liked the idea of the rig on three counts. The first was that it was easy to put together: three 8mm bottom baits and a cork ball trimmed to the required balance. The second was that it was 'in yer face' and difficult for the carp to ignore. The third was that I liked the mechanics of it (hook down) and felt it would be difficult for the carp to eject – if it was willing to suck it in. As it turned out they were willing to have a go at it and it worked beyond my wildest expectations: I had a stunning winter and spring using the rig, and have since had success on it on other waters.

m most comfortable using the set-up with small baits but during a frustrating session at Raduta when Simon Crow and I were being plagued by grass carp I decided to fish the stack using two 8mm baits topped by a pop-up, reasoning that a grass carp might have problems picking up a stack because of the shape of its mouth. The presentation slowed the grass carp down, and accounted for a number of good carp, biggest a chunk of a 49lb common.

call it the stack rig, but I guess you could call it a multiple snowman set-up!

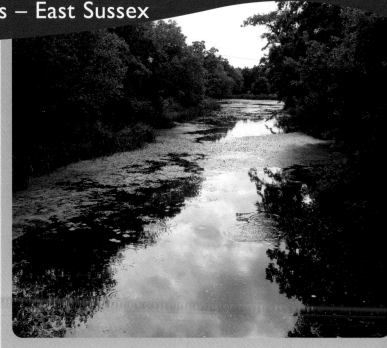

Membership and Contact Details

Membership forms can be downloaded at www.southdown-angling.org

Postal address –
c/o Polegate Angling Centre
101 Station Road, Polegate,
East Sussex, BN26 6EB

Secretary –
Mr H Richardson
☎ 01435 812854

Membership is annual from 1st May to 30th April

Joining Fees

Adult (18 years+) – £65
Spouse of adult – £22
£10 joining fee

OAP/Disabled – £43
£10 joining fee

Young angler (14 years to 18 years) – £22

Junior angler (under 14 years) – £2

No joining fees for young & junior members.

Carp Size

20lb+

Club History/Introduction

SAA was the result of a merger between the Complete Angler Fishing Club in Eastbourne, and Hailsham Angling Association in 1997.

Club Waters

Curls Farm

This is a long, thin lake of 1 acre. Shallow and weed free except for some lily pads and with a maximum depth of 3 feet. Mirrors and commons go to 20lb+ amongst some roach and rudd. Parking is 200 yards from the water (except disabled) and is open all year. 2 rods only. No night fishing.

North Corner Pool

Described as a family water that contains many species, including lots of small carp in the 5lb to 7lb bracket. 1 acre in size and depths to 8 feet. Set in woodlands, the pool has an inlet and a dam, plus disabled swims and easy access. 1 rod only. No night fishing. Open all year.

Hempstead Ponds

Three small ponds, two of which are open for fishing. Ponds 2 and 3 are both about ½ an acre with depths between 3 to 4 feet. There are carp to 15lb in pond 2, and smaller fish in pond 3, with weed in both. 2 rods only. No night fishing. Open all year.

Club Rivers

The Association's bigger carp live in the Rivers and Drains which they control. See page 212 of the River section and page 214 of the Drains section.

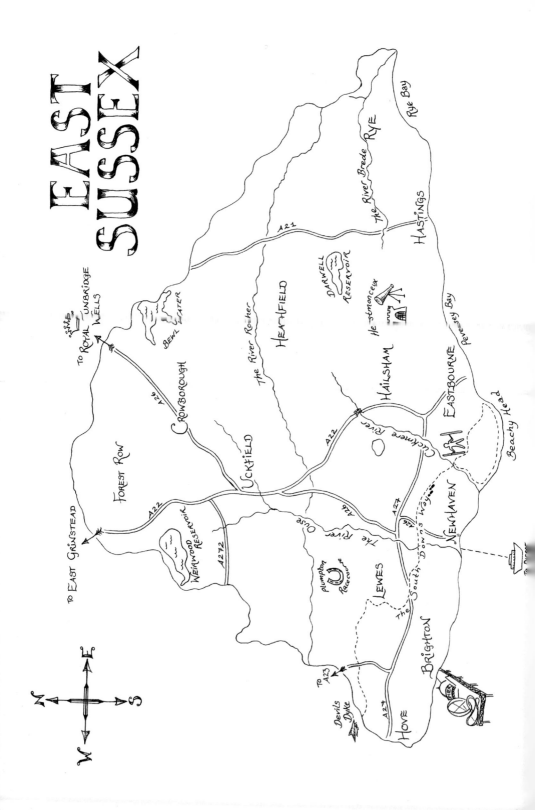

Contents

Broad Oak Fishery
Syndicate – East Sussex

Membership and Contact Details
To apply, complete the application form on the website and send to the address shown
www.broadoakfisheries.co.uk

Membership Fees
Membership is limited to 40 anglers at £500 per year. The season runs from 16th June to March 14th.

Nearest Main Town
Tunbridge Wells

Facilities

Carp Size

45lb+

Broad Oak Fishery near Eridge

Nestled in a valley on a 6000 acre estate on the East Sussex/Kent border, this 14 acre estate lake is situated in splendid, peaceful surroundings. Owned by the Nevill family since the Norman conquests, Eridge Park is designated an area of outstanding natural beauty, and the lake itself, and surrounding area, a site of special scientific interest for its plants and dragonflies. Both Fallow and Sika Deer are prominent in the park, and sightings of barn owls and buzzards are a regular occurrence.

The Lake

Created in the 17th Century by the damming of two streams, it is constantly spring fed, providing cool, oxygenated water even in the hottest of summers. This means that the water level never drops and because of this, and the excellent water quality, there is an abundance of natural food to sustain the fish all year round. Originally known as a tench water in the seventies and eighties, many of the species other than carp have been removed, especially the large shoal of bream that used to be present. At the same time the lake was being stocked with good quality carp from the likes of Mark Simmonds to supplement the original stock of carp present. This introduction brought the carp stock up to around 200 fish in the mid 2000's, with a good percentage of these now over 30lb. The lake produced its first forty in 2007 and that fish is now in excess of 45lb.

Like all estate lakes, the main feature is the margins, of which there are over a quarter of a mile. Depths average 3 to 4 feet with the deepest area, in front of the dam, going down to around 8 feet. There is very little weed and a few lily pads, but all the banks are surrounded by trees, with a large area of reeds on the north bank, where six wooden stages have been built to facilitate ease of casting and fishing.

Facilities

This is a very secure fishery, being almost a mile from the main road, and with two, combination locked gates to pass through before you get to the car park. There is a small fishing lodge as well as a toilet. There is no water tap.

Rules

Standard angling rules apply, but are strictly adhered to and if you break them you will lose your ticket. Amongst them are - no bait boats; barbless hooks only; no lead core but tubing must be used; fishing from designated swims only; no wading; no surface fishing. 3 rods allowed. Most of the rules are common sense, showing respect for your fellow angler and the fish, which is why the requirement for entry to the lake is for 'experienced carp anglers.'

Winter Fishing on Sussex Estate Lakes

by Mark Lawson

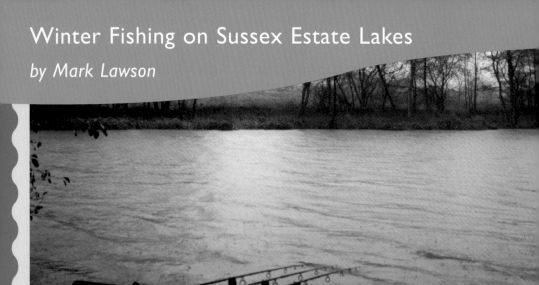

After many years of fishing gravel pits in Kent and the Colne Valley I recently returned to the old estate lakes I'd fished in the 1970's, and some new ones that abound in the east and west of the county.

I have enjoyed very much finding out that all the things I learnt back then still ring true today, so when my old mate Clive asked me to write a few words I thought I would pass on a number of tips that have helped me catch some nice fish, then and now.

A lot of the estate lakes in Sussex are man made, usually in a valley with a stream running through or a natural spring, hence most lakes are fairly shallow, following the contours of the surrounding land. Clay was then used to construct the dam wall or, in some cases, the entire lake bed to minimise seepage. Over the years the stream fed waters slowly silt up to give a silty shallow end at the inlet, deepening towards the dam end to an average depth of about 6 feet. This means that, depending on weather conditions, the majority of the carp will tend to be in the deeper water at night, or in colder weather, before moving to shallower water from around 11am onwards. This is especially so in the winter when most of my estate lake fishing takes place, offering a much better chance of action than on the large pits where the fish tend to hold up in deeper areas which are out of casting range.

If the lake is stream fed a good bet when it rains is where the stream enters, here you will usually find the fish right in the flow looking for food items that get washed in. Another good spot is dead lily pads, if the water contains them the fish seem to love just laying in amongst them whether for safety, or food items that like hiding among the tubers. The margins are always a good spot for a bite and tend to sort out the better fish, however I think that when the fish are not feeding they hold up in the centre of the lake, where they feel safe, but move about looking for food when the conditions are right. This means that the carp you find in the edge tend to be feeding fish and of course the bigger ones feed first, that's why they are bigger. If the water is clear then try putting bait in likely looking areas and keep checking them on a regular basis, if any of the bait disappears take a rod and drop your hook bait in and I bet it won't be long for a bite to be forthcoming. Another fish magnet in winter is ice, carp love to lay under it and as the lake thaws they will follow the edge until it has melted. I have observed this on many occasions when the water has been clear enough to do so. You can see the fish getting more and more concentrated as the ice melts and I have cast a bait from the edge up to 6 feet past it and had immediate bites, it is quite spectacular to see the fish fighting under the ice and smashing it as it comes to the surface. If a small lead up to ¾ of an ounce will pass through the ice when cast, any hooked carp will easily be able to break the ice. If a ¾ ounce lead won't go through do not try with a bigger lead as this means the ice is too thick and will result in a lost carp carrying a rig. Not good practice!

I have lost count of the number of carp I have caught from under the ice after the lake has frozen at night. A good tip is to use back leads right in the margins if you think the water might freeze, enabling you to reach where your lines enter to break the ice. If they are too far out and you can't land the fish you will lose all your tackle, having to pull for a break, therefore leaving baited rigs after you have gone.

Another little edge is to use 1 to 1½ ounce leads and semi fix them with either a lead clip or a stop knot that can slide off. Fish this in conjunction with lightweight sharp hooks. The fish will pick up the bait and move off until it feels tension from your rod and stop, by then your sharp hook should have pricked them and you can then pick up your rod with them just sitting there. I started fishing like this after observing carp in clear water hooking themselves on larger leads and shaking their heads or spinning to get rid of the hook with no indication of a bite at all. You may think a running lead would solve the problem but I think you need to use a much heavier lead for a pivot point, but casting large leads tends to spook a lot of fish so I think the quiet approach puts more fish on the bank - when they know you are about they are harder to catch. Another advantage of the lighter set up is if the bottom is not clean your rig will not sink out of sight, and using half or squared chops also don't sink into any silt as much.

Prebaiting will also give you a massive edge as long as the lake rules allow you to do so. Make sure you put the bait all over the lake and not in certain spots, this way the carp will find your bait wherever they swim. When fishing after baiting, keep the free bait to a minimum and bites will come a lot quicker as the fish will be actively looking for your bait. I do hope that this small contribution has been a help to some of you and encourages you to find your nearest estate lake. They can be very peaceful and rewarding.

Oak Tree Lake
Syndicate – East Sussex

Membership and Contact Details

Mr Ashley Groom

☎ 01892 665351 or 07545 064975

Ashleygroom@me.com

www.thecarpsyndicate.co.uk

Membership Fees

Membership is limited to 50 anglers initially at £300 per year

Nearest Main Town

Tunbridge Wells

Facilities

Carp Size

20lb+

Oak Tree Lake near Tunbridge Wells

Minepit Lake has been an established day ticket water run by Ashley Groom for the past seven years, but Ashley wanted something a little more exclusive, so has done what many carp anglers can only dream of – designed his own lake, to be run as a private syndicate. Oak Tree Lake is a 3 acre lake that has been built by well known lake designer, Steve Burgess. For a lake of this size, there are more features than you would expect to find in a water three times its size, with depths varying from 2 feet along the margins of the two islands down to 30 feet at one end! There are bars, plateaux, depressions and marginal shelves that both the carp and the carp angler will revel in.

Not content with that, Ashley has stocked the water with some stunning carp from the highly commended VS Fisheries, but once again, he has not followed the usual route of stocking with loads of big fish. Instead he has stocked the lake with just sixty carp to low twenties. The idea is to produce a long lived fishery where the syndicate members can grow with the fish, and in such an environment, and with such a good strain of carp, the growth shouldn't be long in coming.

Set deep in the beautiful East Sussex countryside, at the end of a proper mile-long carp track, this lake is for the carper who craves peace and quiet more than the need for a constant stream of big carp in his net. The latter will surely come, but for now there is the rare opportunity to be in at the start of a brand new syndicate, run with old school values – a very rare commodity nowadays.

Membership

The membership is going to be run in conjunction with the Day Ticket membership, so there will be 0 members initially. The full membership will cost £300 and will allow the angler to fish both lakes on a light syndicate. There will only be 6 anglers allowed on Oak Tree Lake at one time, so pre-booking will be essential. There will also be a Days-Only membership which will allow the angler to fish either lake (if space allows). See Day Ticket section on page 30 for costs, under Minepit Lake.

Directions

Full directions are only given out when membership is taken.

Rules

2 rods only. All sessions must be booked in advance. Landing nets, weigh slings and unhooking mats are supplied for your use; do not bring your own. Barbless hooks and safety rigs only. No braided line except marker/spod rod. No particles except hemp seed are allowed, strictly no nuts. No fixed leads, dogs, wading or swimming. All gates to be closed behind you. All litter to be removed from the fishery. Kryston Klin-ik or similar to be used by all.

Pippingford Park
Syndicate – East Sussex

Membership and Contact Details

Mr Richard Morris
☎ 01825 712966
Fax 01825 713638

Postal address: Pippingford Estate Company Ltd, Pippingford Manor, Pippingford Park, Nutley, Sussex, TN22 3HW

info@pippingford.co.uk

www.pippingford.co.uk

Membership Fees

A seasons membership costs £150

Guest tickets cost £10 per 24 hours.

Members may use 3 rods with a 4th at the owner's discretion.

Membership is for all lakes.

Nearest Town
East Grinstead

Facilities

Carp Size

Pippingford Park near Nutley

It is difficult to categorize this venue as the owner describes it as neither a day ticket or a syndicate water, however, as it has a limited number of membership tickets available, it has been placed in this section.

Pippingford Park is a privately owned estate in the middle of the Ashdown Forest, which consists of mostly woodland and parkland, so the surrounding area is tranquil, natural and wild. The estate has been owned and run by the Morris family since 1919, with the fishery starting life in 1936. The six lakes are all SSSI sites with a diverse dragonfly population and also the rare edible frog! Membership is restricted to 100 to 125 members and the venue has a traditional close season (March 15th to June 15th). The first five lakes all feed each other via dams and waterfalls, which eventually feed the River Medway. Disabled access is limited as some of the waters require a long trek from the car park. Night fishing is allowed and members may take a paying guest. The carp record for the venue stands at 36lb.

The Lakes

3 Wards Lake
This is a very silty 1 acre, under fished water described as a general coarse lake. Does hold a small number of commons to 18lb.

Eastwood Lake
An average depth of 3 feet with some areas going down to 9 feet in this 3 acre water. It has 2 islands and is weed free apart from some lily pads. Holds a variety of fish including mirrors and commons to 18lb (there are more commons than mirrors).

Middle Lake

A 3 acre water with depths that average 6 feet and with no weed, although it has a series of large lily pads and a waterfall which feeds the next lake. Mirrors and commons to 30lb+ are present.

Poplar Walk Lake

This lake is 4 acres and has an average depth of 6 feet with an island and large marginal reed beds. There is no weed but there are lily pads. It holds mirrors and commons to 30lb+.

Steelforge Lake

The largest water on the estate at 5 acres, it has 2 islands and depths that average 5 feet. It is quite an open water with no weed and holds commons and mirrors to 30lb+.

Cinder Arch Lake

This 2½ acre water is set away from the others in the east/west valley of the estate. There is neither weed nor lily pads and depths that average 8 feet. It holds both mirrors and commons to 20lb plus.

All the lakes hold other species including large pike, chub, perch and roach.

Rules

Barbless hooks only. Unhooking mats and suitable sized landing nets must be used. All litter to be removed from the estate. Bait boats are allowed. 3 rods allowed. Rods not to be left unattended.

If you ain't on 'em, you can't catch 'em

Ian (Chilly) Chillcott

Waterford Fisheries
Syndicate – East Sussex

Membership and Contact Details
Mr Mick Histed
☎ 01825 830534
No personal callers

Membership Fees
Maximum 10 (sometimes less) £200 per season

Nearest Town
Uckfield

Facilities

Carp Size

30lb+

Waterford Fisheries near Mayfield

This private fishery was set up in 1995 as a fish farm. In total there are 5 waters with only 2 set up as syndicate waters, the remaining 3 are still used to breed fish and are not open to fishing.

This is an exclusive syndicate with a very limited number of memberships, the maximum in any season being just 10, and sometimes less. Waterford has a traditional close season, closing on March 14th and opening on 16th June. Night fishing is not allowed and the gates open at dawn and close at dusk. This is a very secluded fishery in a garden-like setting, with specimen trees and mowed lawns. The owner lives on site.

Top Lake

A small pool of ¾ of an acre which has an island and depths that go down to a maximum of 6 feet. There is an abundance of different weed, and lily pads decorate the water, which is home to a lot of carp. There are commons up to 23lb+ and mirrors up to 27lb+ as well as Koi carp to upper double figures. There are also a handful of tench but no other species. It has only 5 well spaced swims and stalking is allowed.

Bottom Lake

Like the top pool this water is ¾ of an acre with an island and depths that go down to 7 feet. There are lots of plant life as well as various different lily pads. It holds double figure commons, and mirrors to just over 30lb and is well stocked with carp, and only a very low number of tench. There are 5 swims and stalking is allowed.

Rules

Barbed hooks only. 2 rods only. No carp sacks, dogs, fires or litter. Unhooking mats must be used. Rods not to be left unattended. No bait boats allowed. Landing nets are provided. No bait bans but moderate use only.

Weir Wood Reservoir Syndicate – East Sussex

Membership and Contact Details

Mr Mike Smith

☎ 01342 820650

www.weirwoodangling.co.uk

enquiries@weirwoodangling.co.uk

Membership Fees

Syndicate membership is £300

Nearest Town

East Grinstead

Facilities

Carp Size

Weir Wood Reservoir near East Grinstead

Details of this vast Reservoir can be found in the Day Ticket section on page 44. The carp syndicate on Weir Wood has areas that can only be fished by the syndicate members. The number of memberships available is restricted to just 25 and considering that it offers 250 acres of water to fish, you almost have your own lake. Membership allows the use of 3 rods, and also use of the Centre's own boats. These are 15 foot, brand new Pioneer boats with an outboard motor, so moving swims is very easy. The wearing of life jackets is compulsory and all new members must go through a boat training session. Areas such as the shallower south bank can be fished via boats and baiting up from the boats is permitted. There are no bait bans but fish finders are not allowed. Weir Wood Reservoir is under fished by carp anglers and although it has been rumoured to have produced a few thirties it is, without doubt, capable of producing much bigger specimens. Syndicate members also have access to two locked car parks. There are also 20 syndicate pike tickets available

> Don't follow the rest,
> think for yourself. You
> might get your wish
> and catch plenty of fish
>
> Albert Romp

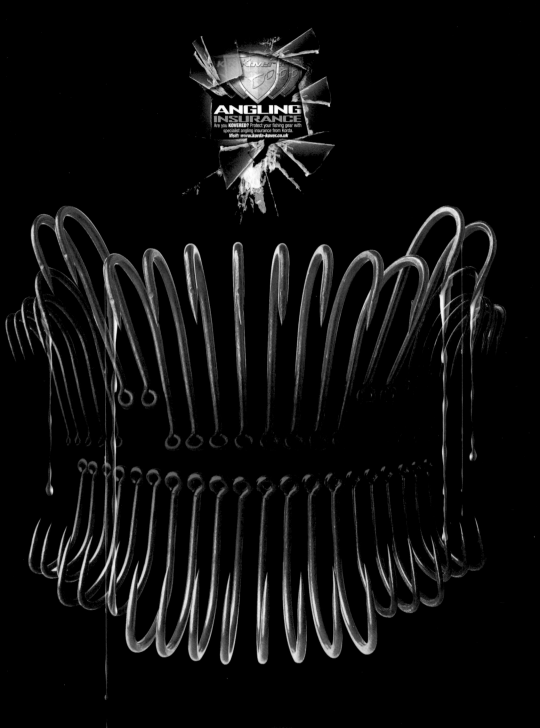

MORE BITE.

White Cottage Lake Syndicate – East Sussex

Membership and Contact Details

www.whitecottagelake.co.uk

elaine@whitecottagelake.com

☎ Elaine 07717 824212

Membership Fees

Two types of membership are available:

Full week membership – joining fee £120

Mid week membership (Mon to Thurs) – joining fee £60

Fishing fees –
£25 per 24 hours
£45 per 48 hours

Longer stays POA

Nearest Town

Hailsham

Facilities

Carp Size

35lb+

White Cottage Lake near Hailsham

This stunningly beautiful 4 acre lake and country cottage are set in private grounds in the east of the county. The grounds, cottage and lake complement each other to the highest standards.

This is a members only water that has an exclusive limited number of memberships available. These memberships are rare and a waiting list is in operation. To even join the waiting list, any potential new member must pay the venue a personal visit. The lake has seven flat and barked swims, all positioned so that anglers do not have anyone directly opposite them, and each covers a large area of water. The depths average 4 feet, down to 9 feet and the lake is weed free except for some lily pads. There are plenty of features to fish to, including overhanging trees, bushes and an island. This is not a runs water but the carp stocks are of exceptional condition and some stunning looking commons and mirrors are present to over 35lb (and growing). The lake also holds roach, tench, pike and big catfish.

All members are issued with a photo ID card and the venue has a secure locked car park. White Cottage provides first class facilities to its members with a purpose built lodge which includes toilet, shower and a kitchen.

Fishing is by booking only and swims can be reserved in advance. Swim choice can be changed on arrival if others are available, night fishing is allowed and long stay fishing is permitted. 3 rods are allowed on this unique and idyllic setting which is open all year.

Rules

White Cottage has a wide range of rules to create an enjoyable environment for all, including the fish. Basic rules are - barbed hooks only; no lead core or braided mainline; no fixed leads; no nut baits or bait boats; no carp sacks; particle baits are allowed but must be properly prepared and are also available on site; minimum 12lb reel line; heavy baiting is not permitted; large mats must be used with a minimum 42" landing net; carp care kits to be used .

The syndicate has its own newsletter

Carpgirls

by Elaine Taylor

What nightmares and dreams are made of!

'I'm one in a million', or at least that's what my family tell me! In all seriousness there are very few female anglers and I have no idea why we don't see more on the bank side.....A lot of guys may say it's for the better, but most I have met over the years are great and happy to fish alongside me.

I cannot think of guys ever being rude to me while fishing in the UK but I experienced some stupid behaviour in France last year and, more disappointingly, the guys were English. I really had to laugh on the last night of our session in France, out of sheer desperation they were dropping their baits right on my marker float. Thankfully their tactics that night ended up nil to the lads and 4 to me. They struggled to catch and having had one fish each by the end of the week, I left with a smile as my partner and I landed 20 fish between us and I had had a lovely 42lb 13oz Common!

I'm not one of those secret squirrels and am always more than happy to share tactics etc. which I find work for me, they only had to ask.

My first fishing experience was around the age of six with my Dad at a local river. I don't remember much apart from getting bored quickly (which in fairness is the norm for kids when not a lot happens; patience is not always a young persons best virtue). Mum and Dad always tried to occupy me on holidays and fishing was near the top of the agenda to pass some time.

I remember going to several fisheries when I was on holiday as a kid. One in particular, I was catching trout by the bucket loads and Dad couldn't pull me away, ended up costing him a fortune. Mum and Dad have reminded me of a very embarrassing photo they have of me standing proud holding my catch, in white knee length socks and a bright orange sweat band - What was I thinking?!

Now at the age of 30+ (blimey time goes) I have very much narrowed down my passion for fishing

Carpgirls

by Elaine Taylor

and dedicate 99% of my time to carp fishing, including eating, sleeping and breathing carp fishing. Obsessed? Maybe, probably, but I prefer to say I'm passionate about it. In my spare time (when I'm not working at my full-time job), I manage the admin, bookings and membership for a local 'members only' lake and thoroughly enjoy everything I do, especially talking with other carp anglers on mutual and common ground.

I have had many a good fishing session, but one which springs to mind is a fishing session on a private lake two years ago. It was a fairly mild March and my partner, my Dad and I had a walk round sussing the lake out and looking for any signs of fish moving or feeding.

We decided on 3 swims next to each other at one end of the lake, as having walked around for a while there were not many signs of fish feeding or patrolling the lake, we also wanted to have a social as well as a good fishing session. I set up camp for the week, wasting no time, eager to wet my lines and start fishing. First night started well, albeit a small 15lb 4oz mirror, I was off the mark. The next day / night all went quiet, couldn't see any movement at all and started to think of different tactics. Never one to sit and wait, I needed to think like a fish to catch one and therefore improve our chances. On the third night still no more fish but an early morning story of an unexpected experience from my partner was some compensation. Waking me, they started telling me they saw something in the night outside walk past their bivvy and with that they started re-enacting the scene, which was highly amusing "I don't know what it was, but it was big and not human. It was this tall and walked like this." By this point I was rolling around on my bedchair laughing "It walked past my bivvy door and all I could see was part of it" pointing to their legs and hips.

"Did you hear it or see it?" they asked. I managed to say "no" in between catching my breath and laughing. "I couldn't even scream or speak, I was paralysed with fear" they said, reliving the fear. By this point I think I should have shown some sympathy or compassion to them, but I was far too busy trying to wipe the tears of laughter away and catch my breath. I mentioned it to my Dad a little later that morning and he said he thought he'd heard a deer walk round his bivvy in the night. Armed with the news, I reported back to my partner and said that it was likely to have been a deer wandering about, thankfully my partner didn't get a run at the same time - not sure who would have come worse off, or more scared, the deer I think.

That day, having only caught one fish on the first night between us, I decided a move was in order but trying to persuade the others was going to be a mission. I walked around the lake again, surveying the water for any tell-tale signs, and seeing more evidence that we just weren't on the fish, I managed to sell the idea to the others it was the right thing to do and move to a different area on the lake. Being put off with moving all their gear, they eventually agreed and that was all I needed. Bivvy down and gear carried around to the awaiting swim, with no time to waste I was back fishing again.

That night, having done the normal routine as dusk falls, the rods were freshly cast, feeling far more confident, everything felt right. As we all retired to our bivvies one last check (as always) on the rods, bait-runners set? Check. Bite alarms? Check. Hangers lined up? Check.....now I can go to bed with the hope that my traps are set and at least one will rip off during the night with a nice mirror or common as the reward for moving.

Dad being the first to catch after the move, not used to large fish and only recently got back into fishing from many years off and never fishing for carp previously, he was wowed when landing a

Carpgirls

by Elaine Taylor

21lb 7oz common. Then came my partners turn, landing a 19lb 4oz mirror later in the day, then again just after dark a beautiful 31lb 1oz common. It was like a pure bar of gold, the deep rich golden glow was magnificent. "So guys, guess you are pleased we moved now then?" I mocked with a smile on my face, now waiting for my turn anxiously.

My turn came the following afternoon. As I was playing the fish, the bailiff who we'd got friendly with on the session came round. Spotting I had a good sized fish before I saw it, he told me "you got a good'un there mate!" "Oh great!" I thought nervously, now I have to tackle my nerves as well as the fish. Feeling a good fish when playing it makes your nerves tingle; to be told it, multiplies the feeling. "Please hook, don't pull" I chant to myself as I feel the line ping every now and again, over the dorsal fin…heart stopping moments. "Ok, I think I'm winning this fight, where's the net?" I ask myself, but before I can say it out loud my partner is there with the fish sliding over the net. "Phew!"now I can breathe and control the shaking from adrenaline rush.

Looking into the net I saw a whopping mirror, in perfect condition and with only a sprinkling of small scales around its wrist and along it's back. I was a proud angler to land a 40lb 2oz mirror, a ʜ ᴍ ᴜ ꜱ ᴄ ɴ ꜰ.

Its then my turn again, just as the sun's going down, I land a 17lb 4oz common. Not a large fish, but the darkest common I have ever caught, deep dark brown with every scale hi-lighted in gold. I was happy; the move was definitely worth it.

I woke up the next day, all of us again having had a quiet night, with the horrible thought of our session coming to an end, just today to go and lugging all the gear back to the van. (Why do us carp anglers have so much gear?).

Maybe we can work that little bit harder to land another fish in our last few hours. I think to myself. Having a cup of tea and a chat, my partner is interrupted by the sound of his bite alarm going… heart leaping and pounding as it screams, another common, 15lb 1oz as beautiful as the 31lber.

As time passes we start to reflect on our session. Not bad for our first session on this lake, a golden 31lb 1oz common and me landing the second biggest in the lake at 40lb 2oz. Then our thoughts and chat are interrupted again, I'm in. Leaping to my feet like a bull in a china shop I rush to pick up my rod, "this feels another lump" dare I let myself think that? I play the fish hoping, like every angler does, that the fish stays on. We both put up a fight, the fish doing all it can to make my

nerves overload once again. As it tires I see I have another near 30lb fish, once in the net I can relax. What a fish! A two tone mirror with star burst scales, hitting the weight of 29lb. Slipping her back to her watery home, my thoughts return to our session, happy and content. Now comes the job of packing up and making our way home, talking endlessly in the van of our tactics, success, and re-living the close encounter with a deer, I am sure the paralysing experience will haunt my partner for many more night sessions to come…

ANGLING SPECIALIST HORSHAM

9 Queen Street Horsham RH13 5AA Tel:01403 264644

Shop Established 1978
FREE parking outside shop

Stocks the following:

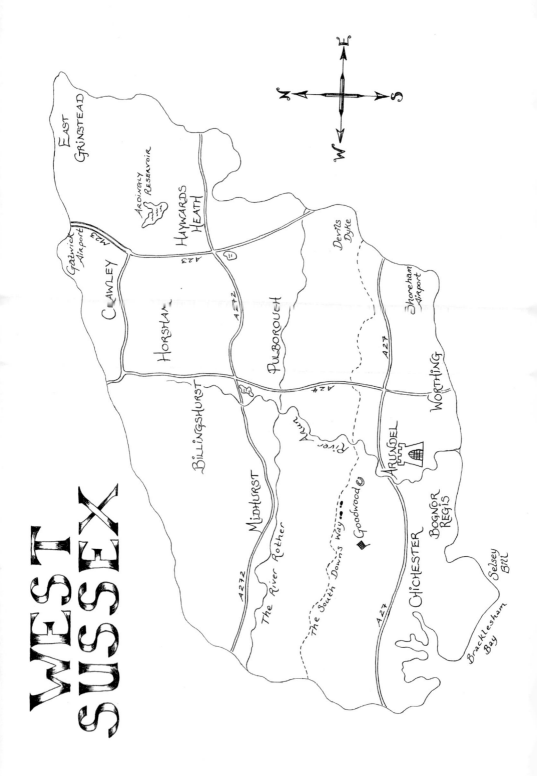

Contents

Alderwood Ponds
Day Ticket – West Sussex

Address
BN44 3AA

Contact Details
☎ 01903 816377
alderwoodponds@hotmail.
co.uk

Nearest Main Town
Steyning

Opening Hours
Summer 7am to 7pm
Winter 7am to dusk

Costs
Day tickets
Adults 1 rod £8, 2 rods £12

Juniors/OAP's/Disabled
1 rod £6, 2 rods £8

24 hour ticket on Island
Pond 3 rods £25

Facilities

Anglers hut

Carp Size

38lb

The Fishery

Two small scenic waters situated in the shelter of the South Downs just outside the town of Steyning and set in an area of outstanding beauty. First established in 1992 with the smaller lake the first to be dug.

Directions

Accessed from the Steyning by-pass the A283. Look for the Ashurst road which is the B2135. Entrance is about 200 yards on the left after turning onto the B2135.

The Lakes

Corsican Pond

This small water is set amongst mature pine trees and is just short of an acre in size. It has 15 swims and depths that go to nearly 6 feet. The margins are littered with lily pads and reeds. There are plenty of small carp present and quite a few doubles, with the biggest common going to 26lb. It also holds ghost carp into double figures and tench, perch and crucians. Day fishing only on this water. Swims 4 and 5 are reserved for disabled anglers.

Island Pond

As the name suggests this 1½ acre clay bottomed lake has a central island, and has depths down to 6 feet. It was dug in 1999 and stocked with numerous commons, mirrors and leathers, with lots of fish in the 8lb to 14lb bracket. There are commons to over 38lb and it has produced a mirror to 31lb. Stocks include perch, roach, tench and a few 20lb+ commons as well as the big one. It is a good runs water and has 26 swims. Night fishing for those over 18 years is allowed.

Fishery Rules

Barbless hooks only. No carp sacks, bait boats or fixed rigs. Unhooking mats must be used. Rods not to be left unattended. No nut baits, and boilies to be used in moderation. Juniors must be accompanied by an adult. No sharing landing nets.

Additional Info

Open all year. Night fishing by booking only. Traditional baits like sweetcorn and luncheon meat work well.

Nothing gets the swim going like maggots, they are the ultimate ground bait even in winter, I use them all year

Rob Maylin

Ardingly Reservoir
Day Ticket – West Sussex

Address
RH16 6SQ

Contact Details
Mr Chris Kinsman
☎ 01444 892549

www.ardinglyactivitycentre.
co.uk

Nearest Main Town
Haywards Heath

Opening Hours
8.30am to dusk

Costs
Both day tickets and day permits are available.

Day tickets – Adult £11
Disabled/OAP/Junior £5.50

During the month of May only, 10 day tickets are available

These cost – Adult £15
Disabled/OAP/Junior £7.50

Season permits run from 1st June to 31st May –
Adult £90
Disabled/OAP/Junior £45

New members – add £30 for Adult & £15 Disabled/OAP/Junior.

Boat hire is £15 per day. Boat users must wear a life jacket

Facilities

Carp Size

30lb+

The Fishery

This large expanse of water is located 5 miles north of the town of Haywards Heath. It has an activity centre which provides all kinds of water sports, including wind surfing and power boating. The reservoir was built and filled in 1978 and for 10 years it was run as a trout fishery only. In 1988 it was opened up for coarse fishing and the trout fishing ceased. A known big pike water that was last stocked in 1998. Some areas are out of bounds to fishing, the dam bank and the west bank are only fishable by boat. That still leaves a vast amount of fishable bank including the scheduled Balcombe arm, whose far margin is castable in many places.

Directions

From Junction 10 of the M23 head towards Copthorne on the A264. Go through Copthorne and turn right at the next roundabout, this is the B2028 Selsfield Road. Stay on this road until you come to the village of Ardingly, where you take the right turn into College Road. Go past the college, which is on the right, and the Reservoir entrance is sign posted on the right. Follow the lane and signs for 0.6 miles until you reach the car park.

The Water

Set in very peaceful countryside, this 198 acre reservoir is in places very deep, with depths going down to a maximum of 45 feet. It has various other depths from as low as 3 feet and a depth map is available onsite. The bottom is mostly clay but areas of gravel can be found as well as bars, plateaux and raised areas. Some margins are steep sloped while others are like a shoreline. Sometimes weed is present. This water holds a very good level of all coarse fish that include roach, rudd, bream, perch, tench and big pike. The carp numbers are unknown but commons to over 23lb and mirrors to 33lb have been caught, despite it being under fished by the carp angler. Boats are available for daily hire and bait boats are also permitted. Night fishing is not allowed. Gates open at 8.30am and close at dusk. Ardingly Reservoir is open all year round

Fishery Rules

Up to 4 rods are allowed but must never be left unattended. No carp sacks, litter, tin cans, tents or fires. Unhooking mats must be used.

Put maggots in self-seal bag; expel the air, compress and seal. They will survive in top nick for 48 hours

Damian Clarke

Daylands Farm
Day Ticket – West Sussex

Address
BN44 3AW

Contact Details
Mr. Derek Crush
after 6pm only.
☎ 01403 711057

Nearest Main Town
Henfield

Opening Hours
Dawn to dusk

Costs
Adults £6
Juniors £3

Facilities

Carp Size

30lb

The Fishery

This is a very secluded, small pool situated in beautiful surroundings. Fishing is by appointment only and numbers of anglers are restricted. A privately owned fishery.

Directions

The farm is near to the village of Ashurst, which is off the A24. Once in Ashurst, take the turning opposite the Fountain Pub, which is School Lane. Keep on this road for almost 3 miles and Daylands Farm is signposted. Follow the track until you come to the farmhouse which is in Honey Bridge Lane.

The Lake

This natural clay bottomed water is about ½ an acre in size. It has 2 small islands and depths of 4 feet. No weed but lily pads are present. 6 swims are available but a maximum of 4 anglers only are allowed.

Carp Stocks
Double figure commons and mirrors to 30lb. Up to 100 fish in total.

Fishery Rules

No night fishing. Barbless hooks only. Unhooking mats must be used. No carp sacks, dogs, fires or litter. No bait boats. 3 rods allowed.

Additional Information

Open all year. Other species present, include chub, roach, rudd and tench.

Five Oaks Fishery
Day Ticket – West Sussex

Address
RH13 7IQ

Contact Details
Mr Mike Parsons
☎ 07801 025342

Nearest Main Town
Horsham

Opening Hours
7am to Dusk

Costs
Day tickets –
Adults 2 rods £8
Juniors/OAP's & Disabled
2 rods £5
Extra rod £2

Adults 24 hour ticket –
2 rods £20
Extra rod at £2
Evening ticket £5

Facilities

Disabled access summer only.

Carp Size

25lb+

The Fishery

This is a private fishery set in peaceful, secluded West Sussex surroundings. The lakes were dug in 1993 and left to mature before being stocked with a variety of species. Although this fishery has now been established for over 13 years it has never been heavily promoted so it has not been over fished and could throw up one or two surprises.

Directions

From the A24, turn off at the Broadbridge Heath slip road and take the A264 towards Billingshurst. This is the Five Oaks Road. Travel for 3.7 miles from the slip road and the entrance to the fishery is on the left, Millfields Farmhouse. From the A29 at the Five Oaks roundabout take the A264 towards Horsham. Drive for 0.5 miles going past Furze View Road on the right and the fishery is on your right.

The Lakes

Top Lake
This lake is only stocked with crucians to over 2lb and some silver fish.

Middle Lake
This clay bottomed lake of about 1¾ acres has 20 small swims. Depths range between 4 to 8 feet. It is weed free apart from some lily pads and the banks are filled with small young trees and bushes. There are also two small islands. The lake has commons to 12lb+ and mirrors to 10lb+ with an estimated total stock of 100 + fish.

Bottom Lake

This lake is also about 1¾ acres and has 18 swims. Depths range from 4 to 8 feet and again it is weed free apart from some lily pads. It holds both commons and mirrors to 25lb+ and there is an estimated total stock of 100+ fish.

Fishery Rules

Barbless hooks only. No keep nets or sacks. All litter to be placed in bins or taken home. Unhooking mats must be used. No bait bans. Bait boats allowed.

Additional Information

The lakes are open all year. Other species include, bream, chub, perch, roach, rudd and tench. No pike or zander.

> Keeping your lines and rigs clean will increase your casting distances. When packing up, reel in through a damp cloth which has a little washing up liquid soaked in it
>
> Bruce Ashby

Furnace Lake Coarse Fishery
Day Ticket – West Sussex

Address
RH13 OQZ

Contact Details
☎ 01403 791163
derekyeates@hotmail.co.uk
www.fisheries.co.uk/
furnacelakes

For bait boat hire call James
☎ 07775 906633

Nearest Main Town
Horsham

Opening Hours
6am to dusk

Costs
Furnace Lake & Pond –
Day ticket £10 for 2 rods.
3rd rod at £5 extra.
24 hour ticket, 3 rods £25

Concessions of £5 per rod
for day tickets only, Monday
to Thursday

All under 12 year olds must
be accompanied by an adult

Roman, Specimen, Kiln &
Plantation –
Day tickets £15 for 2 rods
3rd rod at £5 extra
24 hour ticket, 3 rods £30
Plantation Lake operates a
minimum stay of 24 hours
No juniors under 16 are
allowed on these four lake

Facilities

Carp Size

50lb+

The Fishery

This fishery is right up there with the best stocked and maintained complexes in the UK, let alone Sussex. Boasting 6 lakes in fabulous scenic woodlands, every water is stocked with very big carp and it has been voted the South's top long stay venue.

Directions

Roughly 4 miles from Horsham on the A281 Guildford Road, 14 miles from Guildford. From Horsham travel on the A281 until you come to a roundabout signposted to Billingshurst and Bognor Regis, this road is the A29. Go straight over the roundabout staying on the A281 and the fishery entrance is about ½ a mile on your right and is signposted.

The Lakes

Furnace Lake

This 6 acre lake is the original water. Purpose built swims are constructed alon one bank. It is weed free and is a good water for fishing with floating baits. It holds mirrors to 40lb+ and a good few 30lb+ fish. There are many fish in the 12lb to 20lb bracket and a lot of 20lb+ fish. A runs water during the summer months. Also contains a large head of silver fish.

Furnace Pond

At 2½ acres, this well established pond is the smallest on the complex. It has two islands and is heavily stocked with numerous doubles and at least seven 20lb+ fish with the best so far a 28lb+ common. Described as an ideal water for the novice angler, where blanking in the summer is almost impossible.

Roman Lake

A picturesque 4 acre lake at the top of the complex. There is a large central island that gives all the 14 swims their own water to fish. Has depths that vary from 2 feet along the island margins to a maximum of 13 feet, with various shelves and bars at different depths and is designed for the more discerning angler. Lots of lily pads and good marginal growth. Contains 140 fish between 22lb and 30lb, with 17 known fish over the 30lb mark and 4 40lb+ fish. Biggest is a mirror of 49lb+. The total carp stock is over 200 and it is also home to very big catfish. This lake has its own flush toilet and wooden lodge.

Specimen Lake.

The Specimen lake is 3 acres in size and has depths that go to a maximum of 8½ feet. Areas of 5 feet can be found around the large central island and many large flat areas of 7 feet make up the bottom of this clay bottomed water. There are also many good marginal depths of 5 feet or less. The lake contains nearly 100 doubles, 18 are known to be between 20lb to 30lb and 7 fish go in excess of 30lb. The biggest fish is a 42lb+ mirror. Over half the stock are commons. There are only 8 purpose built swims.

Kiln Lake.

This beautiful 4½ acre lake has many features which include 4 large islands and 4 small islands, plus lily pads and plenty of marginal growth. Maximum depth in this lake is 11 feet, and it is packed with underwater features that range from shallow 2 feet ledges around the islands to flatish areas of 7 feet, and deeper channels. Good margin depths of 3 to 5 feet. Home to over 150 commons and mirrors, with more than two thirds over 20lb, including 30 fish in excess of 30lb. The biggest carp has been out at over 40lb (mirror) and a known 4 other 40lb fish live in this picturesque lake. Shares the toilet and hot and cold running water with Roman Lake and has 18 woodchipped swims and a gravel path.

Plantation Lake

The largest and newest lake on the complex at 6 acres. Like all the lakes it is packed with features to fish to with 9 islands all within casting range and 20 swims that all command their own piece of water. This is the deepest lake at 14 feet but there are many spots that vary right down to 2 feet, including shallow areas around the islands. Stocked with 160 genuine English carp – 80 mirrors that go to 45lb+ and 80 commons to 48lb+ – the lake contains 9 known 40lb fish and 34 others in excess of 30lb. It is estimated that 80 fish range between 20lb to 30lb whilst the remainder are mid to upper doubles. The lake has its own lodge and flush toilet, the lodge also has hot water and a gas cooker and fridge.

Fishery Rules

Barless hooks only. No fixed rigs, bright lights, fires or dogs. Rods not to be left unattended. Unhooking mats must be used. No loud radios or noise. No carp sacks. All litter to be removed or placed in the onsite bins.

Extra rules applicable to Roman, Specimen, Kiln and Plantation Lakes.

One landing net per angler, minimum size 36''. Sharing nets is not allowed. Large unhooking mats must be used. No rods to be left in the care of another angler. No concessionary tickets at any time.

Additional Info

Open all year. Night fishing is allowed on all the lakes. Bait boats available to hire. One non–fishing guest allowed at no charge. Free quad bike tackle transfer for the long stay boys and 3 full time bailiffs, including a night bailiff. This is a very well kept fishery. No pre booking or reserving swims. All the lakes contain other species.

Hunters Lodge Fishery
Day Ticket – West Sussex

Address
RH10 3LE

Contact Details
Mr Paul Vincent
☎ 07812 073435

huntslodgefishery@hotmail.com

www.hunterslodgefishery.co.uk
(updated on a regular basis)

Nearest Main Town
Crawley

Opening Hours
7am to dusk

Costs
Jack's Lake £7 for 1 rod,
£10 for 2 rods
per 12 hours – 2 rod max.
No membership needed

Mick's Lake requires an
annual membership fee of
£30 Then – £10 for 1 rod,
£15 for 3 rods
per 12 hours – 3 rods max.

£25 for 24 hours

Night fishing now available
on both lakes

Facilities

Carp Size

40lb

The Fishery

This day ticket fishery consists of three lakes set in stunning Sussex scenery, in woodlands between Crawley and East Grinstead. Paul Vincent took over what were run down lakes in the autumn of 2005 and transformed them into fabulously stocked and well maintained lakes.– a fishery run by a fisherman.

Directions

Can be tricky to find (the owner likes it like that). Travelling from Crawley on the A264 towards East Grinstead, go past the Copthorne Hotel roundabout for about 1.1 miles and the entrance is located just off the layby on your right. Follow track and signs for 0.6 miles to fishery gates. If you go past the petrol station on the right you have gone past the entrance.

The Lakes

Jacks Lake

This picturesque 1¾ acre lake is described as a runs water. There are 15 flat, barked swims and the lake boasts lily pads and an island but is weed free and has depths to 4 feet. 2 rods only on this lake. The lake bed is clay with pockets of silt.

Carp Stocks

Commons and ghosts to mid doubles. Mirrors to 27lb+.
Estimated total stock – 100s of fish.

Micks Lake

Next door to Jacks lake, this water is 1¾ acres with depths ranging from 2 feet to 12 feet. The bottom is of a different make up to the other lakes as this has gravel spots and bars as well as silt pockets. This is a member's only lake and numbers are limited to only 6 anglers at a time, with bookings required in advance. 13 swims are available amongst lots of lily pads and 2 islands. No weed. 3 rods on this water.

Carp Stocks

Commons to over 40lb, ghosts to 35lb, mirrors to 38lb and all growing.

Estimated total stock about 70 fish.

Rules

Barbless hooks only (max size 6 on Jacks Lake). Micro-barb only on Micks Lake. Unhooking mat must be used.

No braided lines, lead core, fixed leads, plastic leaders.

No carp sacks, zig rigs, dogs, peanuts, tiger nuts, plastic baits.

Minimum 10lb breaking strain main line. Landing nets must be dry on arrival.

All under 16's must be accompanied by an adult.

Mick's Lake is for over 16's only.

A more extensive list of rules is posted on the website.

Additional Information

No close season. Bait boats are allowed but must be used within the area of your own swim only. Other species include golden orfe, tench, perch, roach and rudd. Jack's Lake has pike to 25lb whilst Mick's contains catfish up to 50lb+.

Lakeside Chichester
Day Ticket – West Sussex

Address
PO20 1QH

Contact Details
☎ 01243 787715

Fax 01243 533843

lakesideadmin@
parkholidaysuk.com

Nearest Main Town
Chichester

Opening Hours
7am to 7pm

Costs
Day 24 hours £15
48 hours £25
72 hours £35
Week £60

Season ticket – Dec 31st to
Dec 30th – £350

Tickets can be obtained
from the office at the park
between the hours of 9am
to 5pm or on the bank from
the park bailiff

Facilities

Carp Size

44lb

The Fishery

The Georgian cathedral city of Sussex, Chichester has many gravel pits dotted along its periphery. The Lakeside complex has 11 waters, all open to the carp angler, 10 of these lakes can be fished on a day, weekly or season ticket with the remaining water run as a syndicate.

The complex is described as a holiday park and the pits were originally excavated in the late 1940s to 1950 and were stocked shortly after. The lakes offer a challenge for the novice carper right up to the more experienced angler, with waters to suit all, from the easy runs water to the sit and wait big fish venue.

At the end of 2010 head bailiff Owen Pugh and his assistant Jim Kent began a 3 year work programme to renovate parts of the complex which had, over the years, become overgrown and a bit run down. The aim is to open up areas on some waters that had been closed because of nature's way, and provide more swims to fish and in general tidy up the place. This is a long and hard work programme which will take some time to complete. Some of the lakes will be drained down and the fish stocks will be re-homed into other waters on the complex, whilst some lakes will be re-stocked with the venues own fish stocks from the stock ponds. Whilst the information given was correct at the time of going to print, some aspects of this complex could change over time.

Directions

The holiday complex is situated off the A27 on the outskirts of the city. At the roundabout where the A259 Bognor Road meets the A27 take the Vinnetrow Road towards North Mundham and Runcton. The entrance is a few hundred yards on the right where you will see some of the lakes.

The Lakes

Nunnery Lake

An elongated pool of about 1½ acres with depths of 4 to 5 feet. It has 18 swims and is close to an off road parking area. Plenty of bankside cover and does get weedy in the summer. A mixed fishery with a small head of bream, roach, rudd, tench and perch. But it does hold mirrors up to 28lb and commons to 24lb.

Deep Lake

This small water is to have its big carp removed and transferred to others on the complex. It will then be stocked with a high number of carp up to 20lb. The carp to be removed go up to 34lb. This pool has depths down to 7 feet and plenty of weed growth. Holds a lot of silver fish as well as bream and tench and is designed to become a good runs water in the future.

Triangle Lake

This 2½ to 3 acre lake was recently linked to Ivy Lake but this opening has now been closed and the opening into Copse Lake will follow in the same way. Depths up to 8 feet and holds tench, roach, rudd, pike and perch, plus mirrors and commons which go to 32lb.

Note Nunnery, Deep and Triangle Lakes are the first waters that the team have begun to renovate. More swims will be available and it's hoped that a couple of porta-loos will be located on this side of the complex.

Ivy Lake

The biggest water on the complex at just over 50 acres, this lake is shared by anglers and water sports enthusiasts. The northern basin, as it is known, is reserved for waterskiing and not open to any fishing, this amounts to about half of the lake. The remaining 25 acres (approx) is full of features, including islands in casting range and many bars and gravel humps. It only has 9 swims and holds plenty of the usual species. The carp stocks run to over 200 fish with mirrors being landed to 44lb and commons to 35lb although it is rumoured to have produced larger commons. No fishing is allowed on the road bank.

Copse Lake

Described as a classic 7 acre carp water, where fishing is only allowed on 2 banks. Silt covered bottom with gravel areas and depths down to 6 feet with some deeper spots. It has 10 swims, is weedy in the summer and difficult to fish, but is home to some very hard fighting commons to 30lb and tricky mirrors to 36lb+.

East Lake

East Lake is heavily populated with commons up to 27lb and 2 known mirrors, the biggest weighing 35lb on its last appearance. This 12 acre water is divided by a bar that runs midway across the lake and runs through to the island. The south bank is often the quieter side and sometimes more productive. Described as a good starter water for the novice carper, it also holds some big tench and bream, plus silver fish. Plans are in place to re-stock this water with many more double figure fish.

West Lake

Was once called the Dead Lake as it is under fished and still an unknown quantity. This shallow and weedy water is 25 acres in size and has around 24 swims; the average depth is about 4 feet. 3 banks are fishable and stocks include tench, large pike and mirrors to 34lb and commons to 30lb. Numbers of carp are not known and this water could throw up a surprise or two.

Laythorne Lake

One of, if not the deepest lake on the complex with areas going down to 9 feet. A picturesque 5 acres that has an abundance of flowering lily pads and the summer months see plenty of weed growth amongst the lilies. The carp, which at some time are to all be removed and re-homed within the complex, go to 40lb (a common) and linear mirrors to just over 30lb are also present. Stock also includes some tench, bream, silver fish and some serious sized eels, and it is planned to stock this water with further tench, perch and bream, so it's best to make inquiries concerning the carp stocks if you are considering making a visit. There are 24 swims and fishing is allowed on all banks.

Peckham Lake

Gin clear, shallow and weedy in the summer, this lake is about 3 acres in size and plans to renovate it are in place. The margins have depths up to 7 feet with depths of 3 to 4 feet in the middle. Fishing is from the bridal path and main road bank only. No fishing on the road to the holiday park. Holds a small head of carp with commons to 30lb, other species present are silver fish, tench, pike and the odd bream.

Runcton Lake

0 acres of water that, in places, is quite shallow with areas of 3 feet and a prolific weed growth. The deeper parts are 5 to 6 feet and some areas are found to have thick silt. This is a serious carp water where the known big fish do not give themselves away very easily. It is home to several well known characters such as Black Scale, Boomerang, Cluster and Vince's Pet. These big carp are said to not stay in an area for too long so patience is a must on this water, which is only fishable from 2 banks. There are tench into double figures as well as large shoals of roach, rudd, perch and pike. Runcton is home to roughly 30 mirrors, the biggest of which has graced the banks at 45lb, and it is known to hold about 100 commons which go up to 36lb. There are a good few upper doubles and 20lb fish. This is a possible future syndicate water.

Vinnetrow Lake

The jewel in the crown, Vinnetrow is run as a syndicate water. See syndicate section page 184.

Rules

Barbed hooks only. No fixed or bolt rigs. No bait boats. Unhooking mats are essential. 3 rods maximum. Strict policy on litter, discarded line and tackle. No fires, BBQ's or excessive noise. Anglers under the age of 15 must be accompanied by an adult. Fishing in designated areas only and car parking must be sensible. The bailiff makes regular daily rounds.

Onsite Facilities

Car parking is available in different locations. Anglers may use the toilets on the park site. There is also a water tap on site.

Additional Information

The fishing is open all year. A local Indian restaurant will deliver food to your car but not your swim.

Vinnetrow Memories

by Greg Walker

I first set foot on Vinnetrow around 15 years ago and it was as exciting to fish back then as it still is today. Back in the mid-nineties the lake was a gin clear, weed filled haven containing one or two very special fish (as it still is today). Anglers spent hours trying to fool the monsters then known as Black Scale, the Half Linear, Two Tone, Pop Eye and 2 or 3 monster commons. The fishing was tough and the fish elusive but all that just added to the pull of the place, once Vinnetrow had you hooked it kept you returning time after time.

One of my favourite sessions on Vinnetrow found me and a friend Gary (aka bookworm!) doubled up fishing from the point swim. The point swim has always been popular as it gives you a great view of the lake and offers you many options when the lake is quiet. I had set up for a 4 night session and was fishing the nights on the point swim but spending a large part of the day stalking. It was early summer and the fish could be easily found sunning themselves lying up in the huge weed beds and they were quite partial to a floater, but hooking them was very difficult.

Over the last two days I had found several fish down in the shallows along the Runcton bank and managed to get them feeding on bread and dog biscuits, watching in awe as one mirror in particular (well into the thirty bracket) devoured everything I threw at him. My frustrations rose as every time he neared my hook bait he stopped at the last minute as if to inspect before clearly seeing my hook or line and deciding it was not in his best interest to eat that specific mixer. I spent every night of that session preparing a new presentation for the next day hoping to outwit the big mirror or, if not, one of his smaller friends. The problem I faced is that the average fish I was feeding was at least 20lb+ and with a huge amount of weed present it was not possible to scale the tackle down too light to improve the presentation, as any hooked fish would make mincemeat of light tackle in these conditions. I eventually rigged up with 8lb line and 10lb double strength hook length, a 5gram controller and a size 8 Drennan super specialist hook and once again set off with high hopes, much to Gary's amusement. Once again the fish were present and finally began feeding after hours of problems from the usual army of seagulls, swans and their very persistent baby cygnets – at times it felt like everything was against you. The light was not quite as good as the previous day and I could not quite make out what size of fish were present today other than I currently had three feeding off and on. I flicked my bait out and managed to present it perfectly by 'tweaking' it back to a growth of weed that penetrated the surface, if I could not catch one now I never would!. The fish were working through about twenty baits I'd thrown out and one was headed straight for my hook bait and my heart felt like it was about to make an appearance through my t-shirt. I was almost shocked when the fish took the bait first time without hesitation and this delayed my strike but never the less I'd hooked him! I was using a 1¾lb test curve rod back then for my stalking and the fish powered off straight through two weed beds! However, for once luck was on my side and slowly I managed to coax him out and eventually had him under the rod tip. I could see the fish was no thirty but a common and over the twenty mark, time stood still but eventually I scooped him into the net and with that had a real sense of achievement and relief.

The twist in the story was, that upon shouting to Gary for assistance he was also shouting at me for help as amazingly he had hooked one on the bottom that he had just landed. We had a brace of Vinnetrow carp one mirror and one common, the common caught off the top and the mirror caught on the bottom. The mirror was the fish known as Scaley and weighed in at 26lb and my common weighed in at 22lb, we were both made up. Interestingly Scaley is still present in Vinnetrow today and has been caught at over 40lb a truly stunning fish.

In my time fishing Vinnetrow the most beautiful fish I caught was a 27lb common (pictured), this fish is still alive today and has made it past the 40lb bracket. The biggest I managed was a 34lb mirror caught in 1995 but maybe the most memorable was the smallest fish with the most heart stopping capture.

Vinnetrow is a magical water fished by many great anglers over the years, all with great carpy stories to tell, and this lake is fast becoming a household name in the English carp world.

MBK Leisures – Coloured Ponds & Specimen Pond Day Ticket – West Sussex

Address
GU31 5DL

Contact Details
The owner, Kenny Wright
☎ 07885 754365

Nearest Main Town
Alton

Opening Hours
12 noon to 12 noon

Costs
All tickets must be booked in advance prior to fishing.

To book call Kenny Wright on ☎ 07885 754365

A 24 hour ticket costs £20 for 2 rods, then £15 consecutive days

A 3rd rod costs £5 for 24 hours

Booking the Cabin Swim costs £15 per night

Facilities

Carp Size

30lb+

The Fishery

MBK Leisures have waters in three counties – Surrey, Hampshire and Sussex. The Sussex lakes are right on the Hampshire border, just on the outskirts of the village of Rake. This is a family run fishery that has been solely owned by Kenny Wright since first established in 1979.

Directions

From Guildford going south on the A3, leave the A3 at the Bramshot junction and onto the B2070 to Rake. Turn left at Bull Hill onto the Rogate Road in Rake and within 2 minutes you will see a big fishery sign on your right.

The Lakes

Coloured Ponds

There are five coloured ponds red, amber, green, brown and black. These private ponds are all full of small carp and it's not unusual to catch 20 or more small commons, mirrors or ghosties on a nice summers morning.

The owner describes these ponds as learning waters, perfect for youngsters. All contain lily pads and have an average 5 feet depth.

Carp Stocks

Lots of mirrors and commons in the 3lb to 5lb range. Does produce a few doubles.

Specimen Pond

This pond is just over 2 acres in size and only has 4 swims, one of which has a wooden cabin. Fishing is via bookings only. It has a fairly even bottom in 5 feet of water and a few lily pads. Nobody under the age of 16 is allowed on this pond unless by prior arrangement.

Carp stocks

In total it holds 80 fish, commons to 29lb, mirrors to 30lb+ and ghost carp to 27lb. There are 30 known others over 20lb.

Fishery Rules

For rules on the Coloured Ponds, ask the bailiff.

Specimen Pond rules – 2 or 3 rods may be used. Night fishing is allowed. No carp sacks, lead core, braided line, floating baits or particles (except sweetcorn). Barbless hooks only on this pond. No dogs allowed. Bait boats allowed on Specimen Pond only .

Additional Information

Other species include perch and golden rudd.

Menards Carp Fishery
Day Ticket – West Sussex

Address
RH13 6PG

Contact Details
Paul ☎ 01403 243213
www.menardscarpfishery.co.uk

Nearest Main Town
Horsham

Opening Hours
6am to 8pm

Costs
Membership is essential.
Joining fee £50 for
12 months from joining
date. Renewal fee £35 the
following season.

Fees – 3 rods.
Monday to Thursday £20
Friday to Sunday £25

24 hours £35; 36 hours £55
48 hours £65; 72 hours £85

Holiday tickets – 5 nights
(Sunday to Friday) £125

7 nights (Sunday to Sunday)
£190

Holiday tickets to non
members are available
All fishing sessions must be
booked in advance

Tariffs change to lower prices
for winter fishing from 1st
November

Facilities

Carp Size

57lb

The Fishery

Menards is situated in 10 secure acres of peaceful surroundings on the edge of the magnificent St. Leonards Forest, just outside the town of Horsham. Originally, when constructed in the late 90's, it was two lakes, but it has since been sympathetically transformed into one lake. This is a members only day ticket fishery.

Directions

From Horsham, head towards Brighton on the A281. Once you leave the town look for the Hornbrook public house which is on your right. Go past the pub and Hilliers Garden Centre, which is also on the right, and take the next left which is Doomsday Lane. Go down the hill until the crossroads and turn right at the bottom, into Hammer Pond Road. Drive for ¾ miles and the fishery entrance is on the left. Look for the signpost. The fishery is a good few hundred yards up the lane.

The Lake

This 6 acre water is a carp anglers haven as there are virtually no, so called, nuisance fish, apart from a few small rudd. Set in tranquil surroundings and hidden away in its own world, this lake has many features including 4 islands with plenty of overhanging trees and bushes. Underwater features include gravel bars, plateaux and marginal shelves, and there are also lily pads. Depths vary from 13 feet at the car park end and go up to 4 feet in the Double Bay swim, at the northern end of the water. In all, there are 13 swims, of which six are double plots. Every swim is flat and woodchipped and the footway is barrow proof from the car park to the swim. There is a large head of English carp that have bred very well over the last few years, resulting in a 33lb common that is estimated to be only 6 years old. Total number of stock is unknown but it does hold a large head of mirrors to 57lb+ and commons to 36lb+. The biggest Koi goes 29lb+. Many of the home bred mirrors are heavily scaled and already go into the twenties. Over the next season, plans are in place to remove a number of the lake's home grown commons, this will include all fish up to 20lb. These will be relocated, allowing the other carp to hopefully increase in size.

Fishery Rules

Micro barbed hooks only. No lead core. No fixed rigs. No leaders. No maggot ring clips. No carp sacks. Unhooking mats must be large cradle type (available on site). Minimum 42" landing net. Minimum 12lb main line. Minimum 2lb test curve rod. No nut baits of any kind. No maggots between 1st March and 31st October. No pellets as hookbaits. No disposable BBQ's. No dogs or children. Rods must not be left unattended. A full list of all the rules, including fish handling, can be found on the website.

Additional Information

Bait boats allowed. Open all year. Local take away food can be delivered to the lake. Website regularly updated. The lake also holds some pike.

Mill Farm Fishery
Day Ticket – West Sussex

Address
RH20 1NN

Contact Details
Adrian (Bailiff)
☎ 01798 874853
www.fisheries.co.uk

Nearest Main Town
Pulborough

Opening Hours
7am to dusk

Costs
Hammer & Mill Ponds
Day ticket –
Adults £10 for 2 rods.
Summer evening tickets £5
Juniors and OAP's £5

Specimen Pond – tickets
from bailiff on the bank
Day ticket –
Adults £13 for 2 rods
Summer evening ticket £7
No concession on this lake

Facilities

Timber lodge has ladies,
gents & disabled toilets
and facilities for making hot
drinks and food. Disabled
access is best in summer.

Carp Size

The Fishery

This is a three lake complex set in the grasslands of the 120 acre Mill Farm
and was developed by Mr Jeremy Stuart Smith over 16 years ago.

Please note: this is a day ticket only fishery. Tickets run from 7am to dusk.
Night fishing is not permitted.

Directions

Mill Farm Fishery is situated just off the A29 at Bury about three miles south
of Pulborough. On the A29 head towards Chichester, after passing through
the village of Watersfield take a right turn onto the B2138 signed Fittleworth
and Petworth. Almost immediately is a road to the left which is signed to
West Burton, the fishery entrance is 300 yards past this turning on the left.

The Lakes

Mill Pond

This 3 acre lake has 40 natural swims. It is a very attractive lake with loads of
bankside cover. The lake boasts an island and bays to fish. Depths from just 2
feet to a bowl-shaped average of 4 feet, with deeper water of 7 feet around
the island. The lake is weed free.

Carp Stocks

Commons to 25lb+, mirrors to 28lb+, ghosts to low doubles.
Estimated total stock 300+ fish.

Hammer Pond

Originally this lake, which was opened in 2002, was to be a match lake. But, in the winters of 2009 and 2010 it was stocked with a good head of carp to 20lb so it is definitely not a match lake anymore!

Carp Stocks

Commons, mirrors and ghosts to 20lb.
Estimated total stock 200+ fish and more planned.

Specimen Lake

This lake is 4 acres in size with 18 well spaced swims. It is deeper than the other lakes with depths of 4 to 7 feet. Between the two islands is the deepest water of 10 feet. This is an open water, with very few snags and is weed free. The carp in this lake take floating baits in the warmer months.

Carp Stocks

Commons to 32lb, mirrors to 34lb and ghosts to 32lb.
Estimated total stock 300+ fish.

Fishery Rules

Strictly no boilies, ground bait or method fishing. Barbless hooks only. Unhooking mats must be used. No sacks. No litter.

Additional Information

Boilies might be banned but all particles including tiger nuts are allowed. Bait boats allowed. Halibut pellets are known to work well.

These lakes close to the public on New Year's Day and re-open on the Good Friday of each year.

More House Farm Fisheries
Day Ticket – West Sussex

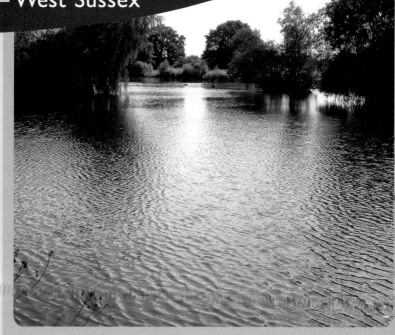

Address
RH17 7RE

Contact Details
Simon Harman
☎ 07800 530173
simon@mhff.co.uk
www.mhff.co.uk

Nearest Main Town
Haywards Heath

Opening Hours
Gates open at 7am and booking is recommended. This can be done online.

Costs
Canal & Sidewinder Lakes
Adults – 1 rod £10
2 rods £12
3 rods £15

24 hours – 2 rods £20
3 rods £25

Concessions for Juniors & OAP's

Kingfisher Lake
Adults only on this lake.
1 rod £10
2 rods £12
3 rods £15

24 hours – 2 rods £20
3 rods £25

No concessions

Facilities

Tackle to swim service is available.

Carp Size

36lb+

The Fishery

More House Farm is set in the beautiful mid-Sussex countryside. There are three lakes which are set in tranquil surroundings, bordered almost entirely by open country side.

Directions

The fishery is located on the B2112 between Haywards Heath and Ditchling, just south of Hayward's Heath, a 15 minute drive from the A23. Situated in Church Lane.

The Lakes

Canal/Match Lake

This lake was built in 2007 with the pole angler in mind. Almost 50 feet wide with 20 swims and depths of between 4 to 6 feet, it is about 3 acres in size. Although it is a match lake it can be fished by carp anglers for the fish which have been growing well since being stocked.

Carp Stocks

Commons to 22lb, mirrors to 15lb. Average size is 7lb and lots of them.

Kingfisher

Built in 1996 and stocked by the E.A. in 1997 this 3 acre water has 17 chipped bark swims. Depths range from 2 to 4 feet with deeper parts down to 8 feet in the island area. Surrounded by green fields and large oak trees, it is generally weed free but does have lily pads. A very peaceful setting.

Carp Stocks

Mirrors to 32lb, commons to 36lb+ and some big ghosties.

Estimated Total Stock – several known 30lb and lots of 20lb with a total of 150+ fish.

Sidewinder

The newest lake on the complex, completed in the spring of 2009, this snake like water has 40+ swims and is almost 3 acres in size with depths of 4 to 6 feet.

Carp Stocks

Commons to 21lb, mirrors to 15lb+ in amongst many hundreds of fish.

Fishery Rules

Barbless hooks only. No carp sacks. No dogs, litter or fires. Particles must be prepared correctly. Unhooking mats must be used.

Additional Information

Open all year. Landing nets, weigh slings and mats are supplied for those fishing Kingfisher Lake, do not bring your own. Other species include roach, rudd, tench, bream and perch.

Don't be lazy, set the alarm and watch the water, this will catch you more fish. Guaranteed

Adam Penning

Passies Ponds
Day Ticket – West Sussex

Address
BN15 0RS

Contact Details
Mr Trevor Passmore
☎ 01273 465257 or
07710 756257

Nearest Main Town
Lancing

Opening Hours
Summer: Dawn to dusk
Winter: 7am to dusk

Costs
Day tickets (all 2 rods):
Adult £10
OAP/Junior £6

24 hour tickets (all 2 rods):
Adult £20
OAP/Junior £12

Juniors (up to 18 years)
fishing nights must be
accompanied by an adult

Facilities

Very good disabled access
including swims to drive to.

Carp Size

29lb

The Fishery

Three lakes near the sea, this is a Centre of Excellence which holds a lot of junior events on all aspects of fishing with a P.A.A. qualified angling coach. Described as a general fishery that stages a lot of match's it does hold some good sized carp.

Directions

Travelling west on the A27 from Brighton go over the River Adur at Shoreham until you reach the traffic lights. Turn right at the lights into Coombes Road and carry on until the fishery entrance, which is on the right.

The Lakes

Main Lake

This clay and sand bottomed lake is 4 acres in size with a little weed here and there. It has an island and depths to an average of 4 feet. There are 50 swims, and it holds lots of species, including commons to 23lb+ and mirrors up to 29lb+

Match Lake

As the name suggests, this 6 acre snake shaped water is designed with the match angler in mind, with 68 platformed swims, no weed and an average depth of 5 feet. It does contain the usual match species but also stocked are a good number of mirrors to 18lb and commons up to 26lb.

Pamela's Pond

A 2 acre water shaped like the letter P, it has an island and 22 swims. This lake is for club bookings and day tickets and has lots of small carp up to 12lb. Described as a juniors learning water.

Fishery Rules

Barbless hooks only. No nut or pulse baits. No plastic baits. Only boilies bought from the on-site shop may be used. No vitalin. Unhooking mats must be used. No carp sacks. 2 rods only on all lakes. Night fishing is allowed.

Additional Information

Open all year. Night fishing is to be booked with the bailiff. Other species in all waters include roach, rudd, bream, tench, perch and chub.

Shillinglee – Lakeside Fisheries Day Ticket – West Sussex

Address
GU8 4SX

Contact Details
☎ 01428 707455

robkaigin@msn.com

www.shillinglee.co.uk

Nearest Main Town
Haslemere

Opening Hours
6.30am until dusk

Costs
Specimen Lake
1 rod £8
2 rods £10
3 rods £12

3 rods allowed from
1st October to 31st May

Day tickets bought on the bankside

Facilities

Carp Size

The Fishery

Lakeside Fisheries is located in the north of the county, only a stone's throw from the Surrey border. The complex consists of five ponds which have been run as a day ticket venue since 1995.

Directions

Travel through the village of Northchapel heading north on the A283. Turn right at the Fisher Street cross roads and the lake will be on your left, after about 1 mile. The car park is just past the lakes on the left.

The Lakes

Silverdale

Formed in 1995 by damming one of the springs that feed the main lake, it is 9 feet in the middle and is used mainly as a breeding pond for the carp. Stocked with small carp to 7lb and a good stock of rudd and tench.

Foxdale

A very pretty, small pond brimming with Golden Rudd which may have some small carp. Open summer only. May to October.

Canal Pond

This pond bas been stocked with about 400 small tench which are gowing fast. Good fun on light tackle.

Specimen Lake

This is the water that will be of interest to most carpers. Set in stunning surroundings, this centuries old lake is 6½ acres in size and has many features, including lily pads, bays, overhanging trees and depths that drop to 10 feet at the dam end, as well as shallows of 2 feet. The lake is also fed by three springs.

Carp Stocks

Mirrors to 42lb and upper 30lb commons.

Fishery Rules

No carp sacks, braid or barbed or micro barbed hooks. No fires. No night fishing. Unhooking mats to be used.

Additional Information

The Specimen Lake now runs a night syndicate. This is limited to 25 members and costs £50 to join, then £20 per night. Members are allowed to use 3 rods all year. Other species include, tench, roach, rudd, perch and big pike.

Sumners Pond – Fishery & Campsite
Day Ticket – West Sussex

Address
RH13 0PR

Contact Details
☎ 01403 732539
www.sumnerspond.co.uk

Nearest Main Town
Horsham

Opening Hours
7am to dusk

Costs
Day tickets:
Adults £8 for 1 rod
£10 for 2 rods

Junior (under 15)
£5.50 for 1 rod
£6.50 for 2 rods
3rd rod allowed at bailiffs
discretion

To fish after dusk you need
to become a member

Details & costs on
application

Facilities

Camping and caravan field
separate from the lakes.
Lakeside pitches available.
Disabled access. Other non
fishing facilities.

Carp Size

33lb+

The Fishery

Established in the late 1980's, this is not your ordinary day ticket water. Sumner Ponds are 8 acres of well stocked waters catering for all types of angler. It is also a campsite for camping with tents and motor homes and there are four lakeside pitches which are exclusive to the booked angler and family. Set in tranquil countryside, the site boasts high quality facilities that include something for the whole family, not just the fabulous fishing on offer. And it does hold some very good carp. Dogs are welcome.

Directions

From Horsham follow the A264 towards Billingshurst and Bognor Regis. Pass the Toyota garage on your right and immediately after the humpback bridge, turn left onto Itchingfield Road and follow through the village of Barns Green (about 2 miles). Entrance to Sumners is on the right, past village pub and stores, which are on the left.

The Lakes

The Small Pond

Just under an acre in size and stuffed full of fish. Commons and mirrors of over 25lb have been caught, this is an easy runs water with plenty of doubles to be caught.

Top Match Lake

This is a 3½ acre water at the top end of the farm, away from the main facilities but it has its own toilet and car park. There are three islands and plenty of flat and firm swims. It is heavily stocked with all sorts of fish including tench, barbel, roach, rudd and lots of mirror carp (no commons). The biggest goes to 25lb and is backed up by lots of mid doubles and fish in the 6lb to 9lb range. An easy runs water.

Sumners Pond (The Big Pond)

This is the water that has the exclusive pitches available. It also has swims for pre booked night fishing. This superb looking water looks as though it is in somebody's back garden, with cut lawns and tropical plants. It has two islands and is just over 4 acres in size and contains a good number of carp, with commons to 33lb+ and mirrors to 30lb+. It also contains ghosties and a high number of doubles, but it is not as easy as the other two lakes. 3 rods may be used at the bailiffs discretion.

Total carp stocks in all the waters is unknown but all have a good head of fish. It is advisable to book the fishing on this lake.

Fishery Rules

Barbless hooks only. All nets must be dipped. Top Match Lake has its own dip tanks. No carp sacks. No fixed leads. Running rigs only. All fish to be treated with respect. Unhooking mats to be used. No floating crust. No more than ½ kilo of groundbait. No night fishing.

Additional Information

Open all year. All lakes are weed free. Bait boats allowed on the Big Pond. A new match lake is now open but contains only silver fish. Pay on bank.

Wintons Fishery
Day Ticket – West Sussex

Address
RH15 0DR

Contact Details
☎ 01444 236493

alanetherington@
wintonsfishery.demon.co.uk

www.wintonsfishery.com

Nearest Main Town
Burgess Hill

Opening Hours
Day: 8am to 6pm
Night: 7pm to 7am

Costs
Membership costs £70

Kingfisher Lake
Daily £30
Night £30
24 hr session £50
48 hr session £70
72 hr £80
Week (Sunday pm to Friday pm) £120

Mallard and Heron Lakes
Daily £15
Night £15
24 hr session £30
48 hr session on Mallard £60
48 hr session on Heron £50
72 hours on Mallard £80
72 hours on Heron £60
Week on both lakes £120

Facilities

Carp Size

49lb+

The Fishery

This fabulous carp fishery was established in the mid 1980's by the Etherington family and is still today owned and run by Alan and his team of bailiffs. It is a members only day ticket venue which is open to all. It is the home of some stunning big carp so there is a high demand for swims on this fishery and fishing is by **bookings only.**

Directions

Just on the outskirts of Burgess Hill, towards the south of the town it is less than a mile from the station in Folders Lane, which is the B2113.

The Lakes

Heron Lake

There are 15 flat, dry and comfortable swims on this well kept 2½ acre water. It has a series of small islands and depths that range from 4 to 7 feet and there is no weed. Contains plenty of commons and mirrors that go to over 30lb and also stocked are very big cat fish.

Kingfisher Lake

At 2 acres, the smallest on the complex, there are 13 swims on this lake and it is deeper than the others, going down to 11 feet, with shallower areas of 6 feet. There are 2 islands and the lake is home to mirrors and commons to 40lb+, the biggest mirror weighing 49lb.

Mallard Lake

The biggest on the venue at 6 acres, this one has 20 flat swims and depths of between 4 to 7 feet as well as 2 islands. There are mirrors and commons to over 40lb as well as some giant catfish. As with all the waters there is no weed present.

Fishery Rules

There are a whole host of rules which are designed to protect both the well being of the angler and the fish. For the full listing go to the website. Some basic carp rules are as follows – barbless hooks only, micro or crushed barb hooks are not allowed. No braided mainline. No lead core. 2 rods only. Rods not to be left unattended. 50" minimum landing net. All nets and weigh slings must be dipped before use. No particles except sweetcorn, hemp and low oil pellets. No alcohol allowed on the premises. No dogs.

Additional Information

Open all year. Memberships run from 1st April each year. Takeaway food is allowed for delivery to the gates of the fishery up to 9pm. Wives and girlfriends entitled to joint membership. Portable BBQ's may be used. The fishery also supplies its own particle and spod mixes for purchase. Wheelbarrows provided for tackle to swims. Winton's support and raise money for the Disabilities Trust.

Keep it simple. The carp are only as clever as the angler fishing for them

Martin Locke

Woodpeckers Coarse Fishery
Day Ticket – West Sussex

Address
RH10 4TA

Contact Details
☎ 01293 886598

E-Mail:- fish@
woodpeckersfishery.co.uk

Nearest Main Town
Crawley

Opening Hours
7am to Dusk

Costs
Adults £7
OAP/Disabled/Junior £5
2 rods
Night fishing is described as
'for regulars only'

Facilities

Barbecue facilities on both
Woodpeckers & Osprey
lakes. Cold drinks available.

Carp Size

27lb+

The Fishery

This is a privately owned and run fishery not far from Crawley, and set in beautiful, peaceful woodland. It was first opened in 1982 by David and Dianne Lucas, when the first pond was dug - Penny's pond. Since that date another three ponds have been dug, leading to what the site now offers today – 4 ponds.

Directions

The fishery is situated off the A2220 Copthorne Road. Look for Old Hollow Road then look out for the blue and yellow sign on both sides of the fishery drive.

The Lakes

Penny's Pond
A small pond ideal for children, with lots of carp to 3lb.

Newts Predator Pond
As the name suggests, this pond holds perch and pike, but also present are carp to 18lb+.

Woodpeckers Lake
A beautiful water of about 3 acres that has 30 swims. It contains quite a few carp to 27lb+, including commons, mirrors and ghost carp. There is no weed but there are two or three sets of large lilies, and reeds at the far end. The lake is quite shallow, no more than 4 feet deep, so float fishing and floating baits work really well.

Ospreys Lake

This lake was constructed in 2001 and is a similar size to Woodpeckers, although it is quite different as it has a number of small islands that can be fished from, which are linked by bridges. It is the deepest lake on the site, going down to 6 or 7 feet in places. There is no weed, or lily pads and it holds carp to low 20lb, with a good number of them.

Fishery Rules

Barbless hooks only. No carp sacks. No boilies or nuts. No dogs, litter, radios. Fishing is from marked swims only. Juniors under 16 must be accompanied by an adult.

Additional Information

It is recommended that you phone first as sometimes the whole complex is booked. Other species include roach, rudd, bream, tench, perch, pike and chub.

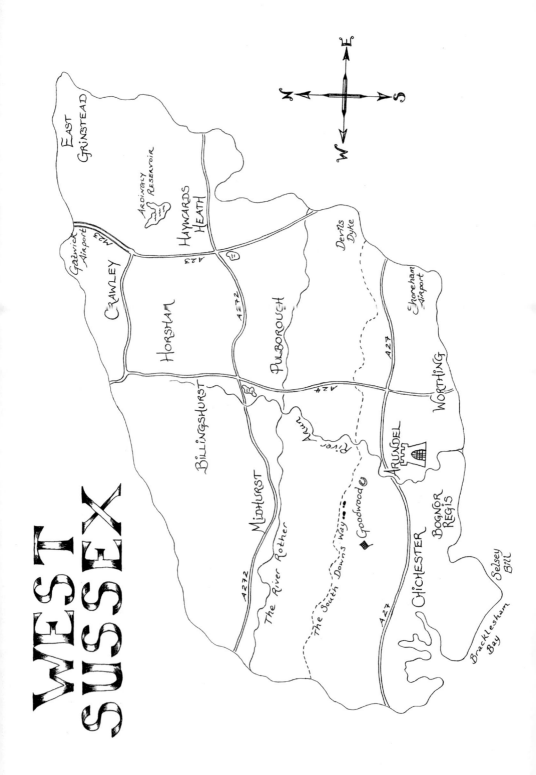

Contents

Billingshurst Angling Society
Club Waters – West Sussex

Club History/Introduction

Established in 1919, the Society caters for a wide range of anglers on their scenic river and stillwater venues, from six miles of the non-tidal River Arun to stillwaters at Billingshurst, Wisborough Green and Northchapel. The Society certainly has something for all types of anglers.

Waters

Jubilee Fields

This small pond in Billingshurst is designed to have easy access for children. Stocks include crucians carp.

Malthouse Upper and Lower Lakes

Both lakes are around 5 acres in size and tucked away in peaceful surroundings. The top water has a huge head of commons and mirrors that go to 24lb. The lake is clay bottomed and has depths up to 10 feet. A good doubles and runs water which also contains tench, perch and crucians. The lower lake holds mirrors and commons to 20lb but not as many fish as the top lake. No night fishing allowed and there is a 2 rod rule.

Shillinglee Lake

Not to be confused with the Shillinglee Day Ticket water, this water is on the opposite side of the road to the day ticket venue. This stunning 3½ acre estate lake has depths that range from 4 to 14 feet at the dam end and is surrounded by woodlands. It holds mirrors and commons to over 40lb. The total stock is unknown but it also holds tench, bream, roach, rudd and pike. Weed free but has a number of lily pads. Night fishing is allowed.

Club river

Details of the six miles of the non-tidal River Arun can be found on page 198 in the River section.

Membership and Contact Details
☎ 01932 583630

info@cemexangling.com

www.cemexangling.com

Joining Fees

The cost of a yearly Gold ticket on this venue is £325

A waiting list is in operation – phone to add your details

Bait boat permits cost £25 per annum

Membership runs from 1st April to 31st March

Carp Size

40lb+

History/Introduction

Difficult to place in the commercial fishery or the club section as CEMEX Angling can be classed as both. A very well run angling company that offers a wide range of venues that are available in 3 different categories - day ticket, season ticket and Gold ticket. The company started life as Leisure Sport Angling around 1969 and once produced a member's newsletter called the Echo Sounder. It changed its name to RMC Angling until the 06/07 season, when they became known as CEMEX Angling. Aims are to create attractive, secure, well-stocked and environmentally diverse fisheries. Their waters once held 5 different British records so it's fair to say that those objectives have been achieved. Always looking to improve, CEMEX Angling have 2 venues in Sussex, one a stillwater the other a stretch of the River Arun.

Waters

Westhampnett Nr. Chichester

An open gravel pit of some 60 acres that is available as a Gold ticket venue, the water is shared with a water sports centre. It can get weedy in the summer and has depths of around 8 to 12 feet, although the area at the water sports centre goes down to 17 feet. Said to hold around 400 plus carp, in the 09/10 season some of the smaller commons were removed and a stocking of 15 double figure fish were introduced, these new fish are said to be piling on the weight. It holds 2 or 3 fish over 40lbs, the best a mirror going just over 43lb and the biggest common to date is just over 39lb. There are 6 other known upper thirties and 20 others over 30lb. Also present are some large erch and bream. There are 20 to 25 easy access swims, some of the swims are classed as double swims. Open all year. 3 rods and bait boats are allowed.

River Arun

or details on the River Arun see page 198 of the Rivers section.

Chichester & District Angling Society
Club Waters – West Sussex

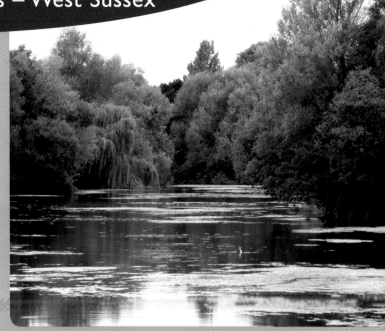

Membership and Contact Details

Application for membership is open to any person who lives within a 12 mile radius of Chichester. If you live outside that area you can apply for associate membership, whereupon you will go onto a waiting list. These memberships are limited. The season runs from June 16th to April 13th. Application forms are available from local tackle shops.

Postal address
CADS, P.O. Box 3231, Littlehampton, Sussex, BN17 6YB

☎ 01903 713084

www.chichester-as.co.uk

Joining Fees

Adult (over 16 years) – Entrance fee £50 plus annual subs of £85

OAP's – Entrance fee £22.50 plus annual subs of £42.50

Junior (under 16 years) – Entrance fee £10 plus annual subs of £20

Under 12 years pay entrance fee of £7.50

Toilet and gate keys are compulsory at £17.50

Carp Size

45lb

Club History/Introduction

The CDAS was first established in 1947 with 21 members. Since those early days this modern and progressive club has gone from leasing a lake to owning their own complex, with very well maintained and stocked waters on the edge of the cathedral city.

Waters

Quarry Lake

A 10 acre lake with a loose, sandy bottom and silt spots. Shaped like a boot and with 39 swims, it has depths up to 6 feet at the A27 road bank end, before it slowly slopes up to the shallow end. A mixed fishery with vast amounts of skimmers, bream, tench, roach, rudd and pike as well as an estimated stock of 200 carp to 27lb, with a good head of 20lb+ fish. There are lots of commons between 7lb to 15lb amongst some very large lily beds.

Whyke lake

14 acres of water and described as Whyke 1 and Whyke 2, although they are really one water with a narrow single channel which allows the fish to move between the lakes. The slightly smaller Whyke 1 has 22 swims and is the deeper of the two and can get very weedy in the summer months. It has a small island, both deep and shallow areas and a few plateaux and gravel bars. The deepest water is found in swims 12, 13 and 14.

Whyke 2 has 18 swims and a large island. This is the shallower side and is pretty much even bottomed, fairly silty with some weed. Both sides of the lake are packed with natural food which has seen the carp stocks pile the weight on over the last few seasons. There is anything up to 25 different 30lb mirrors and commons up to 39lb, plus a good number of fish over 35lb and plenty of 20lb fish. The lake received a fresh stocking of 25 young fish in the 7lb to 12lb range in 2010. Other species include tench and double figure bream.

Churchyard Lake

A gravel pit of 8 acres, with 31 swims, it has deep margins down to 12 feet in places after the club removed the silt. Shallow areas are found around the lily pads in the middle of the water and at the car park end, and there are also two islands. This lake is always extremely weedy through spring and summer and holds big shoals of rudd and a few tench and pike. Home to about 60 carp, mostly mirrors which go to almost 45lb, with maybe another 5 or 6 known 40lb. There are also around a dozen fish in excess of 30lb, and others up to 20lb+. Not many commons but has produced two to 39lb+. Described as difficult to fish.

Long Lake

The lake covers an area of about 2½ acres, has 35 swims and is described as the club's premier match water. Stocked with lots of carp, bream, tench and smaller silver fish, the commons and mirrors run to 12lb+ with a few upper doubles. A good runs water from all the species present. Has deep and shallow areas and is silty but said to be easy to fish.

Little Long Lake

A carp free, 1 acre lake which was once part of the Long Lake. Does hold some good crucian carp.

Additional Information

A well run club with swims suitable for the disabled angler. Onsite complex car park, toilet block and water tap. Members can purchase guest tickets.

Copthorne & District Angling Society
Club Waters – West Sussex

Membership and Contact Details

The club works to a season of 1st June to 31st May each year. No discount for late joining.

Membership forms can be downloaded from the website.

www.copthorneangling.co.uk

richamp@aol.com

Roy Hurley

☎ 07540 350334

Joining Fees 2010/11

All waters, including Piltdown

Adult £68

OAP's £34

Juniors free, but must be registered & accompanied by an adult

Piltdown permit only

Adult £28

OAP's £14

Juniors free, but must be registered & accompanied by an adult

Carp Size

30lb+

Club History/Introduction

A traditional, non-commercial society established more than eighty years ago and based in Copthorne near the town of Crawley, the society has 5 lakes near to Copthorne and one to the west of Crawley. It also shares 8 miles of the River Ouse with the Ouse Preservation Society. It is predominantly a match club, but if peace and solitude and the chance of a carp or two is what you require then this club could be right up your street. All waters have no access to the general public.

Waters

Little Rowfant Lakes

4 lakes, of which 3 are fishable, they all contain mirrors and commons. The best fish are to be found in the big lake where they go to 20lbs. These clay bottomed lakes have depths that average between 3 to 5 feet. Night fishing is only allowed in matches. There is a locked car park. These are very under fished lakes that are described as holding mostly carp.

Rowfant Mill

This is the Club's largest water and is full of all sorts of fish. 20 plus acres in size, it's an established lake with plenty of bankside cover, depths of 3 to 4 feet and lots of lily beds and is relatively under fished . Commons and mirrors to 20lb have been reported but it's believed that bigger fish exist, it also holds some good pike and tench. Locked car park.

Note Both the above waters operate a close season which runs from 14th March to 1st June. Night fishing is allowed.

Copthorne & District Angling Society
Club Waters – West Sussex

Mount Pond

This hard to find, acre plus pond is situated in Ifield, Crawley. It has 2 small islands, lily pads and holds a good head of small carp making it ideal for youngsters. Fishing for juniors is free but must be registered with the club and they must be accompanied by an adult. Locked car park.

Note *No boilies or nut baits are allowed on the above venues.*

Piltdown Pond

This reed fringed 4 acre lake lays near a golf club east of Haywards Heath. Piltdown only permits are available from the club at a reduced rate. The lake holds commons and mirrors to over 31lb and several are known to go over 20lb+. Other species include, big pike, bream, tench, perch and crucians.

Night fishing is allowed. Boilies and nuts are also allowed on this water which is open all year. There is an official car park on site and the venue is on public land.

Club Rivers

Details of 8 miles of the River Ouse can be found on page 207 in the River section.

Ballast Pit Wildies

by Keith Jenkins

When I moved down to Crawley in 1980, my carp fishing was in its infancy. In South London I had little to invigorate my fishing, so tended to concentrate on trips to the Thames at Kingston in pursuit of the shoals of gudgeon and skimmer bream, perch and roach bashing at Tooting Bec pond, or the occasional jaunt to Old Bury Hill in search of tench and crucians. But when we moved to Crawley I was suddenly surrounded by loads of water, and it all held fish. I remember going in to Jack Frost's and chatting with Mick about places to fish and him telling me about the Silt Lake, Campbell's and the Ballast Pit.

I was just tentatively stepping out with carp in mind, so Mick's tales of the hard fighting wildies in the Ballast Pit really caught my attention, and I decided that I would start my initiation there. And what an initiation! The lake was like something out of the Jurassic period with old, dead trees sticking out of the water everywhere, the pit just having been left to flood, with no thought to clearing it of trees and snags. There were only half a dozen swims on there, although a precarious trip along the railway bank would afford a cast into a clearer area of lake, you just needed crampons and strong rope to stop you from sliding into the lake!

The hair rig was about a year away from being publicised so I concentrated on my favourite form of presentation, with a 3BB waggler. I tried sweetcorn, luncheon meat and even made up some cat food paste, all of which the carp devoured greedily, but my idea that the hook should be buried and hidden from view meant that, invariably, the half a dozen or so bites I got resulted in maybe one or two being hooked. The average size of these manic carp was 2 – 3lb, but the power they built up in those tight, snag strewn swims meant learning very quickly how to play hard fighting carp. The largest carp I landed from there was probably no more than 4lb but I really felt that I earned every ounce of every fish I caught from there. A year or so later I went back armed with the hair rig and the results were remarkable, but it didn't mean the percentage of carp landed was any higher – they still fought as if their lives depended upon it.

Most of the dead trees and snags have been removed now, and a lot of the original wildies have passed away, but I believe a few of each remain, and probably scare the hell out of the anglers on there, no matter how well prepared they think they are.

There are so few places like this around now, more's the pity. What a way to learn how to fish. Priceless.

Jack Frost Tackle

Tel 01293 521186 / 421351

www.jfonline.co.uk

Reynolds Place, Crawley, West Sussex RH11 7HB

One of the largest retailers in Sussex & Surrey

Crawley Angling Society
Club Waters – West Sussex

Membership and Contact Details

Download membership form from www.crawleyanglingsociety.co.uk

Postal address – Secretary, 49 Salisbury Road, Tilgate, Crawley, Sussex RH10 5LK.

secretary@crawleyanglingsociety.co.uk

Telephone club secretary
Mr Simon Clark
☎ 01293 467064. Evening calls only – 7pm to 9pm

Memberships can be made at all the local tackle shops

Joining Fees

Membership runs from the 1st May each season

Adults (18 years and over) – £65
Junior (17 and under) & disabled – £35
Husband & wife – £80
OAP's – £20

Half season tickets available from 1st November to 30th April.

Adult – £33
Junior/disabled – £18
Husband & wife – £40
OAP's – £10

All OAP's are allowed to take up to 2 guests at £8 per day

Carp Size

44lb

Club History/Introduction

Crawley AS was founded by the late Mr David Wild in 1956. The club has 3 stillwaters around Crawley and members can take advantage of a ticket exchange with 12 other clubs, giving access to over 90 waters. Exchange tickets are free.

Waters

New Pond

This lake is situated in splendid surroundings, nestled in a valley in the Tilgate Forest. Approximately 4 acres in size, with depths between 4 to 6 feet, it is mostly reed fringed, with a few patches of weed. Night fishing is allowed Monday to Thursday only. This is a mixed fishery with mirrors and commons up to 20lb, and other species include tench, roach, rudd, bream, perch and pike. 2 rods only. There are 30 swims and secure car parking with a locked gate.

Ballast Hole

Night fishing is allowed on this 3 acre venue which was once a gravel works. There are 30 swims and an average depth of 4 feet. It is a clear and weedy water with some snags and holds lots of small carp up to 10lb, as well as a few originals that go to 15lb+. Other species include pike, roach and tench. 2 rods only.

Buchan Pit

Known by the locals as Buchan Park, the real name to this public water is Douster Lake. It is approximately 5 acres in size and has depths going down to

14 feet at the walled end. There are some lily pads and a shallow area which is fishable. It's believed that the carp stock is low, at around 25 fish but around eight of these are 30lb+ fish, with a common of 38lb and a mirror of 44lb. There are a few small commons plus roach, rudd, bream and pike. Night fishing is not allowed; dawn to dusk and 2 rods only. This water has a traditional close season – March 15th to June 15th.

Footnote *Just prior to going to press we learnt that two 30lb+ mirrors had been found dead.*

Campbell's Lake (Tilgate)

At the time of going to print it was unsure what was to become of Tilgate Park. Due to damage to the dam wall, this 17 acre lake has been drained, to allow the dam to be mended, and all of the carp have been removed to a couple of holding ponds. With carp to over 30lb, this was a very popular and prolific water; whether it will be so again remains to be seen. We recommend you contact the club about the future of this water before planning a visit.

Tilgate Memories

by Margaret 'Maggs' Dommett

It was a beautiful morning, just a few days after having snow fall to the ground. The sun was out and I had a day off work. I sorted out my tackle and loaded the car for the short drive to Tilgate Lake around midday and had a walk round to see if I could see any fish movements. As I strolled round I threw a few Sensa probiotic boilies in a number of different spots and waited for a while, hoping to see a few carp that were willing to feed but none arrived. I chose a swim on what is known as the boat house side of the lake, next to the booms which signify the no fishing area. My first rod was baited with a single 18mm bottom bait and cast out into open water, about 20 yards. My second rod was cast just off the boom and was baited with a single bait that I had cut in half and hair rigged back to back to create a butterfly effect.

It wasn't long before I had a belter of a take and for a good five minutes the fish ploughed away in the margins before sliding into my net. A friend, called Craig, had turned up to watch the final moments of the scrap and he kindly looked after my prize while I prepared the weighing and photo bits and bobs. At 18lb it wan't the biggest carp I'd ever had the pleasure to land but it was certainly a very pretty, fully scaled mirror and a very welcome winter fish. After watching it waddle off into the murk I recast the rod with a new half bait to the same spot and put the kettle on for a brew. About 20 minutes later my buzzer burst into life and I was in again. This felt like a better fish as it dived, trying to throw the hook, under the boom. Heavy side strain coaxed the fish back to my net and I landed a second fish in the shape of a lovely 21lb mirror. The hot rod was rebaited as before and flicked to the same spot along with a handfull of free offerings and I remember thinking to myself that although I'd had a right result it wasn't over yet, as a fish rolled just the other side of the boom.

Within half an hour the same rod ripped off yet again and as before I knew instantly that the culprit was not one of the many Tilgate Bream. After a good 10 minute fight I slipped my net under another fully scaled mirror. At first I thought I had re-caught the same earlier fish but on closer inspection noticed it looked a bit bigger. So instead of slipping it back without weighing it I slipped it into the sling – lucky I did as it went bang on 20lb and just like the other one was a true stunner.

The hot rod went through the same procedure as before and it wasn't long before I latched into another carp in the shape of a 19lb winter coloured golden common.

I couldn't believe the afternoon I'd enjoyed. I'd only been at the lake for a couple of hours and I'd managed to bag 4 fish, something that was difficult to achieve in the summer let alone the winter. So, after the common, I went home for a nice hot cup of coffee with a big grin on my face.

Buchan Park

by Chris Frappell

I fished Buchan Park for around 3 years on and off, using it mainly as a local stalking water. Buchan is around 5 acres in size with around 25 carp in it going up to 40lb, you can only fish Buchan from the 16th of June until the 14th of March as it has a traditional close season on it and is also a day's only water due to Crawley Angling banning night fishing, but night fishing may be reintroduced in 2011.

I remember one summer when I had a half day at work and decided I was going to have a little stalk up Buchan. The weather was lovely and sunny, but mild perfect weather for stalking up Buchan.

I turned up at the lake around 1 o'clock and there was a guy coarse fishing by the boat hut and one carp angler set up in a swim called Chris's corner, so I took a walk down the left hand bank looking for fish as I went.

I got as far as the totem pole when I saw a silt cloud in the margin and on closer inspection I saw there were 3 fish coming in and out of the cloud, tearing up the bottom next to the pads by a bush. I went into the next swim and started to get my gear out but, as per usual, I was fumbling and took twice as long getting my rod ready. I decided to present a snowman rig, with a 15mm bottom bait and a 10mm hi-viz pop up, around 15ft from the bank, just left of the cloud. I waited 'til the fish moved under the bush and placed my bait, sprinkling around 5 baits for attraction, then played the waiting game. The fish kept coming in, having a dig in the silt, then would swim off in a big circle and, after about 40mins, it looked like they had gone. I put the kettle on, thinking that after a nice cuppa I would have a move and see if I could find some other fish. I was sitting back with my cuppa when I got a single beep and before I could put my tea down the bobbin smacked into the blank and the tip bent round. On striking I could see fro m the line angle that the fish was heading under the bush. I had to lock up and hope I would win the tug of war, luckily the fish went out into open water. shaking its head trying to get off - she was not happy. After a few minutes I had her nearing the bank, but as I went for the net the fish decided she was off, but this time down the left hand margin which luckily was clear and, after a hairy few minutes, I managed to get her back under control and towards the net. I could see as she went over the cord, and kissed the block, that she was one of the big girls and on looking in the net recognised her as a fish we call the Ill mirror, easy to recognise due to it having massive bulging eyes.

By this time I had an audience of dog walkers behind me, asking what I had caught, so I did the honourable thing and said it was only a little one so they would all leave. I got my bits ready then called my friend, Craig, as he only works local, to come do some pictures for me as I was pretty sure this fish would be the biggest I had had from Buchan. When Craig turned up we weighed her and the scales went 30lb 12oz, my biggest from Buchan at that point. I was well chuffed.

We took some quick snaps while the odd dog walker went past asking "did you catch that in here?" a question you will get asked at any park water when you have a fish. I just always reply "no love, it's from Tesco" and they walk off with a puzzled look on their face. We put her back and she swam off to sulk whilst I sat down with Craig to have a cuppa and tell him how I caught her, over-exaggerating as you do. I was well chuffed - been on the lake an hour and had one of the big girls already. Craig was on his way back to work, and on walking past the boat hut he saw some bubbles which looked very carpy so decided to let me know. I packed up and had a look, but by the time I got to the boat hut they had gone so I decided to do another lap of the lake but didn't see anything.

I was sitting on the wall at the end of the lake thinking to myself, if I see a fish crash I'll stay, and was just getting ready to go when I saw a fish stick its head out in the middle of the lake. I rushed round to a swim called the Lifebuoy, which was the closest to where the fish crashed, and as I walked into the swim it crashed again. My mind was made up, I was going to stay for another go.

I got both rods out, casting them either side of where the fish had crashed, around 40 yards out. This area was around 10ft deep and to my knowledge there was not much there, just silt, so I catapulted around 20 baits over each rod, leaving the rods on the deck with the reels upside down.

About half an hour had passed and a few fish had crashed over both rods but were heading away from the spot. I kept looking at my reels hoping for one of them to start spinning but nothing was happening.

My attention was grabbed by a dog jumping in the lake in the next swim and the owner shouting at the dog, and as all of this was going on I could hear a clutch and, realising it was my right hand rod, I picked it up, took up the slack and the fish was on. This fish was just giving slow lunges and staying deep, the fight didn't take long and within minutes the fish was in the net. On looking in I couldn't recognise the fish so I left her in the net while I sorted my gear and called my other friend, Si, to come take some pictures.

Si popped down and on looking in the net said it was a fish called Black Eye, that was between 24-26lb, so we got her out and the scales went 26lb 2oz. We took some pictures and slipped her back to fight another day.

At this point I was on top of the world; two fish in a day a very good days fishing at Buchan for me, something I hadn't done up there yet. Buchan's not an easy lake to fish and my best year so far was ten fish, so two fish in a day is good going.

If you're looking to fish Buchan Park you will have to join Crawley Angling Society to do so and make sure if you're fishing for carp you have the right gear. There are big carp and lots of snags, including pads, so be prepared when attacking Buchan so no fish are harmed.

Tight lines

Haslemere Angling Society
Club Waters – West Sussex

Membership and Contact Details

Membership forms can be downloaded from the website.

www.haslemere-as.co.uk

Forms are also available at Grayshot Tackle

Joining Fees
Adults – £70
Disabled/OAPs – £27
Junior – £22
Family – £95

Husband & wife tickets and student tickets are available

Carp night tickets cost £10 with work party or £55 without work party

Carp Size

30lb+

Club History/Introduction

This is a Surrey based club that has 2 stillwaters in Sussex. Founded in 1936, Haslemere AS has around 200 members and caters for the leisure, match and specialist angler. The club has no day tickets available on any waters.

Waters

Bicknell Pond

Formally known as the Channel Pond, and once part of Shillinglee Lake, this was renamed in 1998 in recognition of the years of club work by Alec Bicknell. This lake of 2½ acres is separated from Shillinglee main lake by a causeway, with vehicle access over it. This is a narrow water with 30 swims and depths that average 3 to 4 feet, covered in many areas by an abundance of lily pads and said to be under fished by the club's carp anglers. 2 rods only and night fishing is allowed. It holds a good stock of carp with fish to mid 20lb. Dedicated disabled swims available from the car park.

Shillinglee Lake

This tranquil water is owned by the Society and is 25 acres in size. There are 65 swims of differing variety, ranging from reed surrounded platforms to swims in the woods and on the causeway which divides this and Bicknell Pond. It has 2 islands and no weed. The average depth is 5 to 6 feet, with depths at the wall end down to 10 feet, whilst around the islands it is 2 to 3 feet deep. It holds shoals of bream as well as roach, tench, rudd and pike. The carp stocks are said to be reasonable, with both mirrors and commons in the upper double bracket, including a few 20lb+ fish with the water record at 30lb+. Shillinglee is a SSSI site and does have a close season, although the club is in negotiations to open all season. To carp fish at night, members must apply for a night carp ticket. There is a long waiting list for these. 2 rods allowed, with 3 in the winter.

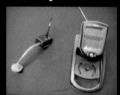

Hassocks & District Angling Society
Club Waters – West Sussex

Membership and Contact Details

Membership runs from 1st April each year. Download form from www.hassocksfishing.co.uk

Postal membership from Mrs J Fisher, 38 Western Road, Burgess Hill, Sussex RH15 8QN
☎ 01444 235978 (before 9pm)

Secretary – Steve Mahkonen
☎ 07915 302354

Membership can also be made at the following tackle shops:- Uckfield AC, Burgess Hill AC, Prime Angling, Percy's of Lewes and Squires Tackle.

Joining Fees

Adult (18 to 64 years) – £70

Husband & wife – £94

Family ticket (including 2 children) – £114

OAP's/Disabled – £40

Joint OAP's – £54

Junior (10 to 17 years) – £32 no joining fee

NB: New members joining fees applicable at £10

Carp Size

30lb+

Club History/Introduction

Founded in 1955 by George Cragg and Bill Bailey and having its roots in the older Burgess Hill Angling Club. The club controls 5 miles of river bank, 5 lakes and 2 smaller waters that are all exclusive to members. Most waters are in the mid-county area, close to the towns of Burgess Hill and Haywards Heath. The club caters for all types of anglers from match to pleasure and specimen anglers.

Waters

Wildings Lakes

This fishery comprises of two lakes, the larger being the club's primary venue for the carp angler, this elongated water is 2½ acres in size and has depths to around 10 feet. It is tree lined with bushes lining the banks and many lily pads and overhanging trees. It holds both commons and mirrors to 30lb+. The smaller lake is about 1 acre in size and holds fish to double figures. Other species include tench, bream, roach, rudd, chub and crucians. Night fishing is allowed. Car parking is on site.

Decoy

A fairly shallow lake of 2½ acres, surrounded by woodlands it has central reed beds and an island and depths up to 4 feet. Fishes well in the summer with floating baits, and produces plenty of double figure fish with commons to 25lb+. On site car park. Night fishing is allowed.

Masons

This clay bottomed lake is 6½ acres and has 60 swims. A shallow water of just 2½ feet with extensive reed beds. Another good floater fishing water that is home to a large head of wild commons, with an average weight of about 5lb although it does contain double figure mirrors and commons, but the wildies are the dominant fish that are said to battle hard. Night fishing is allowed.

Pickwells

Two 1½ acre lakes that have only recently been acquired by the society. Both lakes have an island and depths in places to 12 feet. Carp stocks are unknown but both do contain some carp. Night fishing is allowed.

Mill Pond

This water is 1½ acres in size and has 25 swims and an abundance of natural features, including overhanging trees, bushes and numerous lily pads throughout its elongated shape. A picturesque lake which is quite shallow, although deeper water can be found at the island end, it holds fish up to about 16lb. There is onsite parking and night fishing is allowed.

Hickstead Lakes

A new acquisition for the society. 2 lakes of 2 acres each, named Dovecote and Bullrush, these are relatively shallow waters that were stocked with carp in 2008 which now go to 12lb+. Bullrush is the deeper water. No night fishing on either lake.

The Ponds

Two small ponds aimed at the young or inexperienced angler. George Cragg Pond is a carp free water except for some crucians. Stephen's Pond is a shallow water fringed with reeds and lilies and holds small commons and mirrors. Ideal to get started on.

Club Rivers

Details of stretches of The Adur, Arun and Ouse can be found in the River section on pages 195, 199 and 207.

Additional Information

Some waters are open all year, this varies from season to season. Juniors under 12 must be accompanied by an adult at all times. The club also run a membership permit exchange with many Sussex clubs and Societies. The use of a third rod is allowed after 1st October. Night fishing must be booked and a maximum stay of 36 hours is allowed on all waters.

Haywards Heath & District Angling Society Ltd
Club Waters – West Sussex

Membership and Contact Details

Memberships for Deaks, Balcombe & Valebridge run from 3rd April until 14th March each season.

Slaugham Mill Pond is closed from 14th March until 1st June.

Membership application form can be downloaded at www.hhdas.com

Membership Secretary Mr Jim Ford
☎ 01444 484583 or 07947 571699

jimford1956@hotmail.co.uk

Membership can be made at Burgess Hill Angling Centre. Membership forms available at Jack Frost Tackle and The Tackle Warehouse, both in Crawley.

Joining Fees
Prices are given on the application forms

Carp Size

25lb+

Club History/Introduction

This heart of the county society was formed by a handful of local fishermen in 1912. It now owns several stretches of the River Ouse and looks after the fishing on 3 good sized lakes and 2 small ponds, all within easy reach of the A23 and the town of Haywards Heath.

Waters

Valebridge

Valebridge is described as the club's flagship water. A simply stunning 6 acre lake in beautiful surroundings, it has scattered sets of lily pads in fairly shallow water, with depths of 2 feet to about 5 feet at the dam end. The lake holds plenty of mirrors and commons to just over 20lb with lots of high doubles, and floaters work well in the summer. Other species include tench, skimmers, roach and rudd. Night fishing, pellets, particles and boilies are all allowed. There are 40 swims and onsite parking through padlocked gate.

Balcombe Lake

This 10 acre lake is surrounded by trees and sits just to the north of Ardingly Reservoir. Depths vary from 2½ feet dropping down to almost 9 feet at the open dam end. There are lots of features to fish to, including overhanging trees, reeds, bars and deep channels. Carp stocks are not that well known by the club, but it has produced mirrors to over 20lb and commons to over 25lb, there are lots of doubles also present. It also holds large numbers of bream, tench, roach, rudd and perch as well as pike into the twenties. Special rules apply on this lake, details in member's handbook. Night fishing is allowed and there is a car park.

Slaugham Mill Pond

A beautiful, peaceful water of nearly 17 acres, with depths to 5 feet. At one time this lake had a large snaggy area which was impossible to fish and the ongoing removal of these snags since 2001 has seen the fishable area increase in size by almost 6 acres, although some safe holding spots for the fish still exist and are out of bounds. It has a few strange rules for the carp angler: i.e. night fishing allowed to a maximum stay of 24 hours but no bivvies, also no boilies, nuts or particle baits allowed. Because of the rules and the out of bounds areas it's not fished a lot by carpers. Stocks are unknown, but it has turned up fish in the upper twenties and is thought to have bigger uncaught fish. There is an onsite car park.

Deaks Lane

These two small ponds are both under an acre in size and are ideal for the youngster or beginner with carp to double figures. Restocking has taken place on the bottom pond, with fish to 6lb and plenty of F1 carp. It also holds tench, roach and bream. No night fishing.

Club River

The club owns several stretches of The River Ouse, and details can be found on page 206 in the River section.

Henfield & District Angling Society
Club Waters – West Sussex

Membership and Contact Details

Download membership form at
www.henfieldas.co.uk

Postal address:
28 Lucastes Lane,
Haywards Heath, Sussex,
RH16 1LF

Tony Carr
☎ 01444 440497

tony.carr@henfieldas.co.uk

Joining Fees

Adult £64
OAP's/Disabled £30
Husband & Wife £78
Family Ticket (2 adults
2 juniors) £92
Intermediate (17-18 years)
£40
Junior (12-16 years) £15
Under 12 £6

Carp Size

18lb

Club History/Introduction

HDAS are a friendly club, based in the west of the county and cater for all types of fishing from match to specimen hunting. Established over 100 years ago, this club is open to all and has in excess of 350 members.

Waters

The Olney Lakes

Ponds 1, 2, 3 and 4 are all small waters half an acre or under in size. These shallow ponds all hold mainly carp up to 8lb, to a possible double. No night fishing allowed.

Olney Main Lake

A 2 acre water that has 17 swims. The average depth is 3 feet with spots going down to nearly 6 feet. There is no weed, but marginal rushes and willow trees give bankside cover. The main stock are commons and mirrors up to 18lb. No night fishing allowed.

Forest Farm

A secluded water of 1½ acres and depths up to 6 feet and 16 swims. There are commons and mirrors to 10lb+, with other species such as rudd and perch. No night fishing is allowed. Onsite car parking

Batts Pond

A small water of about ½ an acre which only has 3 swims. There is weed in places and a few lily pads and depths down to 4 feet. The lake holds plenty of small carp in the 6lb to 7lb range. No night fishing allowed.

West Town Farm Pond

Another small ½ acre pond that strangely only holds one mirror carp of 12lb. Depths of 5 feet and a few lily pads. It is mainly stocked with roach, rudd, tench, perch and a few grass carp into double figures. No night fishing allowed.

All club stillwaters are 2 rods only and are open all year.

Club River

The club control 14 miles of The River Adur, which is home to some very big carp. See page 194 of the River section.

Horsham & District Angling Association
Club Waters – West Sussex

Membership and Contact Details

Membership can be made at the local tackle shop or via postal address.

HDAA, PO Box 22, Horsham, Sussex RH12 2YT

☎ 01403 262255

Fishery officer
Mr Les Eggleton
☎ 01403 260070

www.hdaa.co.uk

Joining Fees

Adult £60
Disabled/OAP's £30
Junior (10-15 years) £10
Under 15 years free

All juniors must be accompanied by an adult

Night permits
2 rods £25
3 rods £40
Night permit holders normally have to have been a member for 2 years
Non-fishing guest £6

Carp Size

30lb+

Club History/Introduction

Established in 1907 this west of the county club has over 450 members. Its stillwaters are open all year and the club describes itself as friendly and catering for all styles of coarse fishing. Members have access to scores of other waters throughout the south as associate members of CALPAC.

Waters

Roosthole

Set in very peaceful surroundings on the edge of the St. Leonards Forest, this 4 acre water is owned by the club and over the years has been stocked with hundreds of carp. A clay bottomed lake with depths down to 12 feet at the dam end, it has very little weed but does have a few lily pads. The average weight of both mirrors and commons is 12lb to 14lb although it has produced quite a few 20lb+ fish, including mirrors to 25lb+, commons to 24lb+ and a 20lb+ true leather. It also holds lots of other species including bream, tench, roach, chub, pike and perch. Night fishing is allowed for up to 3 rods. Swims for the disabled are reserved and there is a nearby parking area. Sometime during the month of April this lake closes for 4 weeks for work parties.

Birchenbridge Pond

The club have been restricted in the amount of work allowed on this stunning looking water of about 6 acres. It is a very silty, shallow lake and half the surface is covered in big-leaved lilies in 2 feet of water. It is under stocked, with just a few carp. A few seasons ago it produced a mirror of 27lb but it's not known if it is still alive or still in the lake. It has also produced a common of

24lb+ and other fish are present but not in any numbers. Other species include bream and pike. Night fishing is allowed.

Island Pond

This is a 2½ acre estate lake set in quiet surroundings. A very clear, clay bottomed water with depths from 2 to 6 feet which does contain weed. It has produced quite a few 20lb+ mirrors and commons, the best common going over 32lb. It was recently stocked with 400 small carp that have doubled in size over the last season. It also holds some big pike. Night fishing is allowed.

Fox Hole Pond

Heavily stocked with small carp, this 2½ acre water has depths to a maximum of 3 feet. It is clay bottomed with an island and a few lilies. The biggest carp is around the 18lb mark, and it does hold lots of fish. Night fishing is allowed, with up to 3 rods.

Sun Oak Farm Ponds

These are 2 small ponds of about ½ an acre each, set on farm land in St. Leonards Forest. This is a Site of Special Scientific Interest (SSSI) so does have a close season. Both pools hold a few carp, the best a mirror living in Dry Pond at just over 21lb. It has also produced a 21lb Koi.

Dry Pond is shallow and quite weedy. The other pool is called Black Bottom which is the deeper water holding tench and carp into double figures.

Club River

The club has access to 4 miles of The River Arun which contains carp. See page 198 of the River section.

Finding Spots

by Clive Williams

Life would be so much easier if, every time we went angling on a new water we could take to a boat in order to find and mark some spots to cast to.

As this is not the case on most lakes we have to use a few tools for the job of 'finding spots'. For me, knowing what depth and type of lake bed my rig is presented on is very important, in my opinion second only to fish location.

The tools needed are a large spooled reel, a stiff rod plus a marker float, lead and plenty of patience. Braided line is an absolute must as it has zero stretch, resulting in far more feeling from the lake bed transmitted to the rod tip as the lead is dragged about, thus making underwater features such as gravel and weed much quicker and easier to find than using stretchy, nylon mainlines. Braids are extremely low in diameter which also helps with long casts if that is what is required.

There are many marker floats to choose from but I find the Korda drop zone marker kit is perfect for all types of lake beds - from clear, weed free clay bottoms to weed infested gravel pits, it does the job without any fuss. Most gravel pits, over the years, have developed a short, soft silkweed that grows to about 6 to 9 inches and on many pits this horrible sticky weed covers the entire lake bed. The Korda kit comes with a buoyant stem which is very useful when fishing waters with silk weed as it lifts the float above the weed. When finding spots on weed free waters the stem can be removed from the set up. The Korda marker kit also comes with a specially shaped feature finding lead.

Gravel is probably the easiest feature to find, whether it be on the top or on the side of a bar or plateax your rod will reveal a very recognisable tap, tap, tap through the rod tip. The more pronounced the tapping the bigger lumps of gravel you have found. If the tip just gently bumps along then that is likely to be a good spot to place a rig. Finding weed is very easy, simply cast as far as you can and with the rod tip pointed at the water surface, slowly retrieve the marker system back and if weed is present you will very quickly find it. The sensation on the rod tip will feel jerky as the lead tears through the weed. The thicker the weed the harder it will be to move the lead. It helps in thick weed to remove the buoyant stem, but if the marker fails to rise then it's probably not a good spot to cast to.

Finding silt, or chod as it has become known, will give you a completely different feel on the rod, the lead will feel as if it's stuck in mud. A gentle pull will bend the tip until you feel the lead slide out. To get a feel of the depth of the chod, watch the rod tip and the more bent the tip is the deeper the silt/chod you have found.

Once you have found your chosen spot, clip the line into the spool clip and have a few casts left and right and if you feel happy and confident with the spot then there is not a lot more you can do except cast as accurately as possible to the marker with your baited rig.

A few general tips. Take your time. Make notes on a new water. Have a cast about for an hour before you go home and mark any spots down for the next trip. A braid of 25lb breaking strain will cast a long way with a stiff rod and a 3oz lead.

Petworth & Bognor Angling Club
Club Waters – West Sussex

Membership and Contact Details

Membership runs from 1st April to 31st March each year.

Download form from www.sussexangling.co.uk

Forms also available from local tackle shops, or postal applications welcome.

Mr M. Harmsworth
☎ 01243 603783

Memberships can be paid in instalments.

Joining Fees

Adult £84
OAP/Disabled/Student £42
Junior (12-16) £20
Under 11's free but must be accompanied by an adult
Family ticket (2 adults, 2 children) £130

Carp Size

25lb

Club History/Introduction

Formed in 2007 by the amalgamation of two clubs - Petworth Angling Club and Bognor Regis Freshwater Club. They control 9 individual waters on 5 fisheries and stretches of the Rivers Arun and Rother. Not all of these waters contain carp.

Waters

Petworth Park

The clubs biggest stillwater at 7 acres, set in the grounds of the National Trust's Petworth House this is a mixed fishery that contains a low stock of mid doubles as well as stocks of tench, rudd, roach, bream and perch.

No night fishing is allowed, fishing is 7am to dusk. 2 rods only.

Stemps Wood Ponds

Stemps Pond

This small clay bottomed water is less than an acre in size. It is well stocked with mirrors and commons that go to 18lb+.

Cart Pond

As above but the fish go to just over 16lb. Both lakes are weed free. Stemps Wood Ponds do not allow night fishing. Fishing is from sunrise to sunset. 2 rods only.

Hurston Lane Fishery

These 3 small lakes are owned by the club and were opened in 2000 by Bob James. Set in lovely, peaceful surroundings, only one water will appeal to the carper.

Carp Pond (Middle Lake)

Night fishing is allowed on this ½ acre pool which has an abundance of lily pads and weed beds and is home to mirrors going to 24lb and commons to 25lb. 2 rods only.

Bethwins Farm

Two small ponds in the north of the county, very close to the Surrey border. Both contain double figure commons and mirrors to about 16lb. No night fishing is allowed. 2 rods only.

Club Rivers

Details of The River Arun and Rother can be found on pages 198 and 208 in the River section.

Location is the key, find them and you have a chance

John Richards

Pulborough Angling Society
Club Waters – West Sussex

Membership and Contact Details

Membership is available from local tackle shops:-
Tidal, Prime and Arun Angling.

Secretary Mr Mick Booth
☎ 01798 831525

www.pulboroughas.com

Joining Fees

Adult £65
OAP/Disabled £35
Junior £20
Husband & Wife £75
Family Ticket £85

Membership runs from
1st April – 31st March
each year

Carp Size

16lb+

Club History/Intrduction

A well established club having been founded in 1919 in the west of the county
The club owns a complex containing 6 lakes which have all, over the last few
years, gone through redevelopment stages. It has over 400 members.

Waters

Goose Green complex

Heron Lake

A 2 acre lake with depths going to 6 feet and no weed except for some lily
pads, it holds commons and mirrors to 16lb+. There are 30 swims.

Canada Lake

10 swims on this ½ acre water and depths to 6 feet, it holds commons and
mirrors to 15lb+

Kingfisher Lake

About the same size as Canada lake, it is weed free and stocked with smaller
carp to 10lb+

New Pond

A small water of just over ½ an acre and depths of up to 6½ feet, it has only
6 swims and a few lily pads. Commons and mirrors to 16lb+ are present.

Deep Lake

This 1½ acre water has been enlarged from its previous size and is the
deepest on the complex at 8 feet, with two small islands. It is stocked with
mainly small carp and a few larger fish.

Tench Pond

As the name suggest it is stocked with tench although it does hold some small carp.

All the lakes contain other species including roach, rudd, bream, skimmers and crucians. Night fishing is allowed at Goose Green. 2 rods only. Toilet on site.

The club also control 2 other small ponds which both hold small carp:- The Mill Pond in Storrington and Duncan's Pond in Pulborough.

Club Rivers

The club has access to stretches of The Rivers Adur and Arun, both of which hold some good carp. For details see pages 194 and 198 of the River section.

Always give floaters a thought, even when it's cold, on top is the best way

Chris Ball

Rother Angling Club
Club Waters – West Sussex

Membership and Contact Details

Download membership form from club website www.rotherac.co.uk

Postal address
Mr C Cobbold
19 Greengates, Lurgashall,
Petworth, Sussex, GU28 9ES
(no callers)

☎ 01428 707670

Joining Fees

Adult
New member £47
Existing member £37

OAP/Disabled/Junior
(16 to 18 years)
New member £33
Existing member £28

Junior (under 16 years)
New member £23
Existing member £18

Carp Size

20lb

Club History/Introduction

The Rother Angling Club is based in the Midhurst area and has been thriving since 1952, although the origins of the club go back over 100 years. Open to all, it has over 200 members. The club caters for a wide range of anglers, including the specialist angler, on stillwaters and rivers in the west of the county.

Waters

New Pond

This 2 acre water was cleaned and dredged a few years ago and has depths going down to a maximum of 6 feet. There is very little weed but there are a few lily beds and the water holds plenty of commons and mirrors up to 20lb. Another smaller water is on site and this also holds a small number of carp into double figures. There are 24 swims, night fishing is allowed and it is open all year. 2 rods only.

Rotherfield Pond

There are 27 swims available on this 1½ acre lake, which has depths up to 8 feet and is weed free. It is close to the River Rother and holds carp to over 20lbs as well as roach, bream and tench. Night fishing is allowed and this water is open all year and does offer day tickets. 2 rods only.

Cooks Pond

A 4 acre water that is the club's match venue. There are no carp except for some crucian carp.

Club Rivers

The club controls sections of both the Rivers Arun and Rother. For details see pages 198 and 208 of the River section.

Burgess Hill Angling Centre
143 Lower Church Road
Burgess Hill
West Sussex
Tel: 01444 232287

Sussex is home to a number of fishing opportunities

Sussex has a wide variety of differing waters and of course we've tried to cover all with the necessary equipment. Being located central to some of the best coarse fishing in the South East, we naturally have a very large selection of tackle and accessories to suit all your needs.

We also have a large range of tackle for the game angler from chalk streams to reservoirs, covering not only this but also salmon fishing with both fly and lure. There is always a stock of our own tied flies and particular patterns can be tied to order. For the fly tier, there is a large selection of materials and accessories.

For the modern specimen hunter we have everything you need, and as well as the tackle we also stock bivvies, bedchairs, frozen and shelf life boilies, carp and trout pellets and ingredients for making your own baits.

As an added service, we know that accidents do happen and generally when it's most inconvenient. To the angler this could mean missing an important match, a planned foreign fishing trip or even just a weekend's pleasure fishing. We offer an in-house rod repair and customisation service. Whether it's a broken rod or ring that needs re-whipping we are able to offer a professional service to get you back fishing as quickly as possible.

These are just a few of the products we hold in stock.

Visit our website: www.burgesshillanglingcentre.co.uk

Slaugham Angling Club
Club Waters – West Sussex

Club History/Intoduction

A local village club formed in the early 1950's which has a limited number of memberships available. Only in recent years has membership been open to all although a waiting list is in operation.

Waters

Furnace

Sitting in very rural surroundings on the edge of the village, this almost 6 acre lake is a highly stocked mixed fishery. There are around 40 swims of which the car park swims are reserved for disabled anglers. Depths on this clay bottome water reach 10 feet at the road end before rising to an average of 5 to 6 feet and a shallow far end of 2 feet. There are many silty areas, no weed but a few lily pads. The lake contains all the usual species including a high number of carp. It has produced 2 mirrors just over 30lb with a low number of 20lb plus mirrors and commons and lots of fish from 8lb up to high doubles. This is described as a runs water with plenty of small fish to wade through. Night fishing is allowed for 2 rods in the summer and 3 permitted in the winter months. There is off road parking on two sides of the lake.

Carters Lodge

This is a long narrow lake of 4 acres set on private land and well off the beaten track, down a long, steep drive. It is very secluded and quiet with plent of bankside cover. This is a deep water with areas going down to 16 feet and an average of 6 to 7 feet. There are around 20 swims and no weed. Like urnace, Carters is a mixed fishery and the carp stocks are unknown although it has produced a common and a mirror to 23/24lb, but the average is 6lb to 9lb, including many small wildies. Juniors are not allowed on this water. This lake is under fished because of the long steep walk as there is no parking at the water. All cars have to be parked in a lay-by and it is not suitable for disabled anglers.

Southwater Angling Society
Club Waters – West Sussex

Membership and Contact Details
For all memberships telephone the secretary.

Mr Chris Hollingsworth
☎ 01403 258594

Joining Fees
Adult £35
OAP's £20
Junior £12

Carp Size

20lb+

Club History/Introduction

A small club whose waters are in the village of Southwater. Formed in 1968 they have around 120 members and membership is open to all. They control the fishing on a park pond and a water which they own.

Waters

Lennox Wood Pond

This is an old brickyard clay pit of about an acre and has around 10 swims. Set in Southwater Country Park it offers fishing on a club membership and day tickets. It is said to hold a few carp up to maybe 20lb. There are depths of 4 to 6 feet with plenty of bankside cover and both lily pads and reed beds. There is an off road car park close by and public toilets on the other side of the park to the pond. No night fishing is allowed. 2 rods only. Good disabled access. Day tickets cost – adult £4, junior £2. It has a traditional close season.

Castlewood Lake

This water is owned by the club and is around 2½ to 3 acres in size. It has 37 swims and is a very deep, former brickyard pit. There are 2 areas of water that are joined by 2 channels which the fish can move between. In places the depths go down to over 20 feet while there are some areas of 6 feet and very steep margins. This is a mixed fishery with no weed and species that include roach, rudd, tench, bream, pike and crucian carp. It does hold a low number of 20lb+ mirrors and commons and a number of doubles. Night fishing is allowed. 2 rods only and open all year.

Soft
N-TRAP
20lb
9.1kg
Weedy Green
COATED HOOKLINK
KORDA

IT WON'T CRACK
UNDER PRESSURE

The eagerly awaited arrival of Korda's new coated hooklink is finally here! After an extensive development period,
-TRAP brings all the latest advancements in coated hooklink technology to your tackle box. Superior knot strength
on overhand loops with a supple inner braid and a super smooth, perfectly colour matched outer coating.
Available in gravel, silt, weed, and 15lb, 20lb & 30lb versions.

AVAILABLE FROM KORDA STOCKISTS NOW! *For more information, klick* www.korda.co.uk

Worthing & District Piscatorial Society Club Waters – West Sussex

Membership and Contact Details

Membership runs from 1st April to 31st March.

Forms are available from local tackle shops.

Postal address
Mr R Baker,
19 Brendon Road, Worthing,
Sussex BN13 2PS.

☎ 01903 763699

www.wdps.org.uk

c.turner540@ntlworld.com

Joining Fees

Adult (18-64) £75
OAP (65+) & Disabled £45
Husband & wife £100
OAP husband & wife £60
Junior (12-17) £20

Non fishing membership £10

Family membership (2 adults 2 juniors) £120 plus £10 each additional junior

Carp Size

25lb

Club History/Introduction

Established in 1955 by a small group of local anglers the club offers a broad spectrum of fishing for the match, pleasure and specimen angler on a limited number of owned and rented local waters. Working with the Environment Agency and local conservation societies, the waters and surrounding areas are kept as natural as possible.

Waters

Laybrook Fishery

A 3 lake complex owned by the club which has secure onsite parking and both ladies and gents toilets. Open all year with a 2 rod limit until 1st October to 31st march inclusive, when 3 rods may be used. Maximum stay is 48 hours. Longer sessions available on request.

Byron

A water of ¾ of an acre and depths up to 6 feet, this is a long slender lake with an average depth of 5 feet. There is no weed but a few lily pads. The club describes this as a match lake with commons and mirrors into double figures present. There are 20 swims and boilies and floating baits are not allowed on this lake.

Milton and Shelley

Listed by the club as 2 waters, in real terms this is one water with a narrow channel that the fish can move through.

Milton

About ¾ of an acre and depths that go from 2 to 6 feet, there are only 7 swims and an island.

Shelley

Shelley is much deeper than Milton, with depths going down to 13 feet. This water is about an acre in size and has a shallow weedy bay, with 12 swims and a few lily pads. Mirrors to 25lb and commons to 24lb share these two bits of water, with a good number of mid doubles also present. Other species on the complex include bream, tench, roach, pike and perch.

Club Rivers

The club controls 3 stretches of the River Arun which have all produced carp. For details see page 198 of the River section.

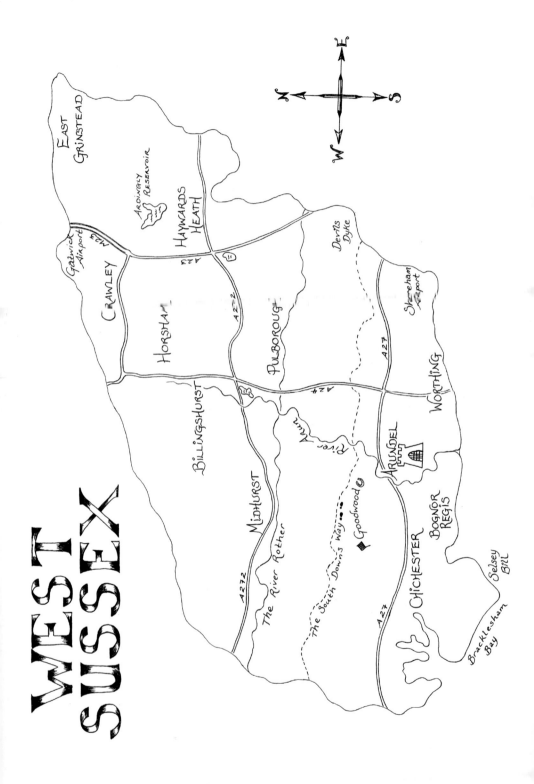

Contents

Borde Hill
Syndicate – West Sussex

Membership and Contact Details

Robin Southon

☎ 01444 412561 or 07746 298508

www.bordehill.co.uk

Membership Fees

All tickets cost £100 Membership numbers are set at 100, with a waiting list if needed. All members will be allowed to take a guest.

Nearest Main Town

Haywards Heath

Facilities

Carp Size

20lb+

Borde Hill

This is a newly set up syndicate for the 2011 season. Borde Hill is open to the public as a garden and park, with all kinds of facilities, including a cafe and country walks. Set in 200 acres of parkland and woodlands in the High Weald area of Haywards Heath, this site is registered with English Heritage. The lakes are set in the south park area, with the use of a designated parking area. The gardens were created in the early 1900's, with plants from all over the world, so the scenery is quite unique.

There are 2 lakes for the members to fish.

Robertsmere

This lake is around 2½ acres and has 40 swims. It is a clay bottomed water, has depths going down to 11 feet and is weed free apart from some marginal reeds. It is stocked with plenty of species including roach, rudd, perch and chub. Commons and mirrors are present, with several known 20lb+ fish.

Harry's Lake

This lake is 1½ acres, with depths up to 12 feet and lots of small carp to 10lb. Night fishing is allowed, but with 2 rods only.

Rules

Most of the rules will be set by the members when the syndicate gets up and running. Basic rules to apply are barbless hooks only. No nuts or beans. No dogs or litter.

M A Wickham Fishing Tackle

Established for 35 years

Shop stocks

HARDY
Marksman Rods

KORDA
THINKING TACKLE

DYNAMITE BAITS

KRYSTON

SOLAR TACKLE

E·S·P

DAIWA

AVID

SHIMANO

BC

CHUB
SPECIALIST INNOVATION

trakker
One step ahead

GARDNER

Freezer baits from:

mainline

H.B.S

Richworth
WHERE QUALITY COUNTS

NASH

Middle Row, East Grinstead, Sussex RH19 3AX

01342 305095

Membership and Contact Details

All syndicate enquiries, including costs should be made to the water controllers.

David & Gillian Hayler, Tripp Hill Garage, Tripp Hill, Fittleworth, Pulborough, Sussex RH20 1ER

☎ 01798 865267

All postal enquiries must be accompanied with a letter, covering angler's fishing history.

Nearest Main Town

Pulborough

Facilities

Carp Size

20lb+

Burton Mill Pond

Burton Mill Pond was formed in the sixteenth century when streams from the downs were dammed to power the mill for the Wealden iron industry.

The area is part of a nature reserve and a SSSI. The water is rich in plant and aquatic life, including newts. Bank access is very restricted, making the fishing extremely difficult. The south west arm of this 30 acre water is reserved as a wildlife refuge and about 10 acres of water are open for fishing from the road bank or the punts available. Syndicate membership is very limited and a few day tickets are available for guests of the members, but must be booked in advance. The water has a history going back to the 1950's, when it was stocked by Donald Leney with a few carp. Famous angler and one time British carp record holder, Chris Yates, has spent time on this water searching for the unknown monsters which are said to have once lived in this lake, and still might be resident. Stocks are low and unknown, because of the difficulty in the fishing, with limited water to fish and an abundance of plant life, including giant lily and reed beds. The Mill Pond lies at the base of the South Downs in tranquil, pleasant surroundings and holds roach, tench, perch, pike and some commons over 20lb+. Night fishing is allowed for syndicate members only. Off road parking. 2 rods only. Fishing must be booked in advance. This water has a traditional close season.

Hawkins Pond
Syndicate – West Sussex

Membership and Contact Details

Hawkins Syndicate c/o Mannings Heath Golf Club, Fullers, Hammerpond Road, Mannings Heath, Sussex, RH13 5PG

Membership enquiries to Julie Hill at above address.

Syndicate organiser:
Mr John Woodhatch
jwoodhatch@crain.com

Membership Fees

£540 the first year
£270 rejoining

There is a fee of £20 to join the waiting list (to deter timewasters), this is deducted from the joining fee.

Nearest Main Town

Horsham

Facilities

Carp Size

35lb

Hawkins Pond

Hawkins Pond is one of the famous medieval hammer ponds, which has an iron ore history going back hundreds of years. These natural sheets of water and furnaces were once littered throughout the St. Leonards Forest and mined for the iron rich clay from the bell shaped pits. Hawkins is a magnificent, 11 acre water set on the border of the forest and is truly a tranquil carp anglers paradise, where time appears to have stood still.

The water was once controlled by the local club (H.D.A.A) but in 1994 the land was sold to Mannings Heath Golf Club and a syndicate was set up. The whole area is a SSSI site, so all the fishing areas are left as natural as possible. In all there are 27 swims, 14 on the Horsham side and 13 on the forest side. All are well spaced, with plenty of small stalking spots between the swims. Depths at the widest point, which is the 70 yard road end, go down to a maximum of 10 feet with an average of 6 to 8 feet of clay bottom. There are large lily pads and marginal reed beds dotted along what is about ¼ mile of water.

Since the start of the syndicate, regular small stockings of Fisher's Pond strain carp have been introduced and this policy still exists today. These fish have taken well to their surroundings and a rapid growth has been achieved by some fish. The biggest mirror to date is just short of 35lb and the commons go to 34lb. The number of 30lb+ fish stands at 8 to 10 with 35 to 40 back up 20lb+ fish. A high number of doubles make up the estimated 240 carp present. The water also holds large pike and perch as well as roach, rudd and bream although plans are in place to remove some of the roach, rudd and bream.

Membership is limited to 70 and a waiting list is in operation. Members have an off road and locked car park. The water shuts on the 1st June for 2 weeks each season for the annual tidy up.

Rules

Rules are kept to a minimum and a high level of responsible behaviour and respect for the fish and surroundings is expected. 3 rods are allowed. All mats, nets and weigh slings must be dry when brought on to the fishery. No boats of any kind are allowed. No Tilley lamps. Well behaved dogs allowed. No wading.

Birthday Bash at Hawkins

by Jason Townsend

I'd managed a few quick over-nighters after work but nothing had fallen to my rods. To be fair the fish that I had heard of coming out from friends etc. were coming out in the day (there you go I've made my excuses)!

So, after being busy at home and the tackle shop, I thought I would set a day aside to wet a line for a 24hrs session and it was going to be the evening before my birthday. Brilliant, there's nothing better than waking up next to the lake and on your birthday to boot.

Anyway, let me tell you about the session. The weather had been wet all day, ideal considering the last few months had been warm and muggy with high pressure leaving the water with not much oxygen so it was a much needed change and, in turn, would liven up some of the bigger fish.

On my pulling up in the car park there were a couple of guys already there, however that didn't worry me too much as there's 14 acres of lake to share. On walking around the lake the swim that looked inviting to me wasn't taken but was being cut off by another angler on the opposite bank. I had thought about the swim before turning up, which I know is wrong but when you get in tune with a lake you fish regularly you get to know where there'll be, of course you get it wrong sometimes but that's angling for you, to be fair these fish don't always show themselves or give themselves away.

Anyway, I had to fall back on my second choice which is called 'dead trees'. The name comes from a few years back when there used to be an old oak directly opposite, which had come down. After it had been cleared away the only thing left to be taken out was the stump, which was taken out at a later date. Since that, another smaller tree has taken its place. It's only a short cast to the far margin in this swim of about 60 yards, with a small patch of pads either side of me. With the nights now drawing in, I set about getting the rods out on the spots. This is made easier by marking the line with pole elastic and because of the tree lined margin, lining up with a silhouette of one of the tree tops. All three rods were baited with my faithfull 15mm garlic and shrimp, finished with 10mm yellow pop ups.

Birthday Bash at Hawkins

by Jason Townsend

The first rod was cast about 12 foot to the left of the fallen tree, about 6 feet from the far margin, in about five feet of water with the lead making a nice little donk on touchdown, 'good enough' I thought. The second was cast hard and low so the rig got under some over hanging branches of the snag, I couldn't quite feel the lead land on that one due to the hard low cast but it was out there, so I was fishing, plus coupled with a helicopter rig and some Gardner foam I was sure it was fine. The third was again cast to the far margin to another tree that had fallen in, but this snag was really in another swim to my right called the Canopy. I just hoped no one would turn up and go in it. Anyway, it landed just shy of them. All rods received two pouches of 15millers which fell tightly grouped around my rigs. I wasn't too worried as I have recently shortened my hook links hoping to nail 'em within the tight bed of boilies.

Once my house was up, and my bed was ready, I set about cooking my lunch which I shared with my mate Gary, who was fishing up to my left in the next swim. Like him, I too was worried that our lines weren't going to affect the fish moving up and down the far margin but we soon forgot about that and started to chat, putting the world to rights and having a laugh, which is really hard not to when Gaz is around as he is funny with a capital F.

It got to about 10 o'clock when I had my first take, which came to my left hand rod, the bobbin pulled up tight and shook. Shining a head torch on the tip I could just make out the line moving to the left, the fish was on and just kiting. On picking up the rod I leant into it straightaway, giving it plenty of side strain and with the rod tip right under the water trying to turn the fish's head. It wasn't long before it had done the trick and she was back to where I wanted her. She broke the surface and I heard the swirl, it sounded big and with the slow lunges she was doing she felt big as well, so I stayed calm and eased off a bit. Gary got the net and put it in the water, and as she started to tire I pulled her in between the nets arms, where Gaz lifted the net around her. I got the head torch and flicked it on and peered into the net to look at my prize - I'd got myself a nice common. I broke the net down and moved up the bank with her, carefully laying her in the carp cradle where we quickly weighed her, with the needle of the scales settling on 28.4oz. With that done, Gaz fired off a couple of shots for the album and retuned her none the worse from her ordeal.

The rod was quickly re-baited and placed back out in the zone, as when the fish do come along the margins and you have one you can sometimes pick another one off if you replace it quickly enough. Anyhow, another couple of pouches of bait were fired out to replace the ones that had been munched.

Not long after, Gaz and I turned in for the night, I wasn't in bed that long before the middle rod let out a few bleeps, and with that a slow, steady take developed. I was on it like a flash and I pulled into the fish trying to gain as much as I could, as well as walking back to prevent the fish gaining sanctuary in the snags. It wasn't long before the fish was in front of me as, once it had realized I was taking no prisoners, it had swam right towards me. At first I thought it was a smaller fish, Gaz didn't muck about and landed the fish thinking it was only a small one. I laid the rod on the floor to organize the mat, sling and scales. In the meantime I could see Gaz shining the head torch into the net, saying that it was certainly bigger than I had thought. I stopped what I was doing and also peered into the net and saw a beautifully scaled mirror, we placed her on the scales and weighed her at 32 pounds exactly. As you'll be able to see, the colour of her was just breath taking. As I placed her in the edge I unzipped the sling and let her get accustomed to her surroundings once

Birthday Bash at Hawkins

by Jason Townsend

again, she took a couple of gulps of water and powered off into the deep margins. Great, two good fish under my belt and it still hadn't reached my birthday. Gaz gave his congratulations and then returned to his swim, I on the other hand was concentrating on getting my rod back out. Once that was done I sat down and boiled the kettle so I could have a much needed brew and could reflect on the last few hours.

After all the commotion that had gone on at the far margin, I wasn't confident of much else happening and if there was to be I was sure it wouldn't come till the morning, still you always need to stay positive otherwise you might as well pack up and go home. Once I finished my last mouthful of coffee I settled down for the rest of the night, just as the rain started to come down. While I was in my bag, all toasty, I chuckled to myself. It's great hearing that rain pounding the brolly and you're under it all dry. I had barely dozed off when I was woken by another take and I ran out into the rain to the rods. I had the rod in my hand and straightaway it felt snagged on something because as I was winding I could feel a grating, my heart was in my mouth. The fish was continuing to pull at the other end, then all of a sudden I felt my line ping and the line went slack. For a split second I thought that it had come off but as I wound down the line tightened and I was back in direct contact with the fish again. The fight was erratic and even when it was close to the edge, and it rolled over the draw cord of the net, I didn't think it was that big. Now, with the fish in the net, I grabbed the torch from my bed chair and flicked it on, shining it once again into the net. I confirmed that it was a good common and was also shocked at the width of her. Rolling it onto its side to get a better look I noticed a patch of mottled scales. I had a peek on the other side and again another patch of mottled scales - it was a fish called Texas which is a 30+ fish. Once I broke the net down and rolled it up I lifted Texas from the margins, my lower back was letting me know it felt big. I called out to Gaz for a hand as this was probably going to be my PB common so I wanted everything to be right. Once in the sling, and up on the scales, the needle swung round to 34.12. Well, now it felt like my birthday so once again Gary fired off some stills for me, and amazing they looked too. As we retuned her and we watched her waddle off under the light of the torch, I was speechless to say the least.

Once again I re-baited and lined up with the opposite bank's tree line, I wanged the rig out to its spot with about 30 to 40 baits. Then I was soon back in my bag for a now much needed rest. Sometime during the early hours of the morning I received a liner, quickly shutting my eyes again but for what only seemed like seconds. I was awoken at first light to a buzzer with the clutch ticking away slowly. The rod was only being held in place by the bank stick placed by the side of it, acting as a snag bar, and the fish was kiting to the left the same as my first catch. I picked up the rod, tightened the clutch, and whatever was on the end felt slow and heavy. Thankfully, none of the fish had given me too much hassle, as this fish also had gone away from the tree snag. Whether it's something to do with the direction they come from I am not sure, but still as I was playing the fish I was very nervous, as well as enjoying every minute of it. The scrap went on for about five minutes and it held its ground and stayed deep until I got it close in, then all of a sudden the fish came up in the water and a big, long common came into view. I had already had the net dipped in the water so I quickly took the opportunity to net it as soon as it rose up again. This time when it rose its big mouth was coughing water out and that's when I had it kissing the spreader block. I lifted the net revealing another birthday present, then all hell broke loose in the net, it soaked me as it went wild. I stuck a pole in between the block and left it to calm down while I got the mat and weighting apparatus ready. I went back to see if it had calmed down, then I broke the net down and rolled the fish up, picking up the rod that laid next to it but supporting the fish from underneath with my other hand. I placed it on the mat where I removed the size 8 long shank, which was right on the edge of the mouth. I slid the fish into the sling and got the now zeroed scales through the handles and slowly lifted, the needle swung round to the 30 pound mark but just fell short at 29.12. I really couldn't have been happier so I placed it in the sack for a short while so it could rest, and then could get some proper morning shots.

Half an hour later I went to wake Gaz from his sleep so he could help out with the photos. He told me that he too had had a carp, so well done to him and a big thanks for being the camera man for me.

Well, there you have it, my BIRTHDAY BASH session ~

Good luck and tight lines.

Horton Club
Syndicate – West Sussex

Horton Club

Sitting in the middle of extraordinarily beautiful Sussex weald and downland, this lake is 4½ acres in size. Situated well off the beaten track, on private open brook land, this picturesque water has depths of up to 8 feet. Established as a clay pit in the 1920's it has 42 platformed swims, with limited disabled access. The bottom has silted up over the years and the lake has a little weed here and there plus a few lily pads. Other features include an island in one corner and controlled reed beds. It contains mirrors to just over 22lb and commons to 28lb, with plenty of back up fish, including ghosties to over 20lb. It has also been stocked with roach, rudd, tench, perch, bream, crucian carp and pike. All memberships run from the 1st April each year and the venue is open 365 days a year. It has a limited membership of 100, with members allowed to take a paying guest. Night fishing is allowed and members are allowed up to 3 rods. Guests are allowed 2 rods only.

Rules

Barbless hooks only. Unhooking mats must be used. No dogs or litter. No carp sacks or nut baits. Minimum 36" landing net. Rods not to be left unattended. Bait boats are allowed. A list of all the rules are posted on a notice board in secure onsite the car park.

Additional Information

This venue is next to a land fill site, where members have the use of the toilet, Mon – Fri, 8am – 5pm. All members are supplied with a key for the locked fishery entrance. The lake pathways are well maintained and barrow-friendly.

Newells Pond
Syndicate – West Sussex

Membership and Contact Details
Mr Tim Cottom
☎ 01403 891424

Membership Fees
£160
A discount applies for any OAP or disabled angler, or father & son membership

Nearest Main Town
Horsham

Facilities

There is also an angler's lodge with a catch log, and a boat house.

Carp Size

29lb+

Newells Pond

This is an extremely old, near 4 acre lake, that dates back over 200 years. It is set in a hollow on private land and in a peaceful rural setting. In 1978 the new owner, Tim Cottom, had the water drained down to remove the years of silt that had reduced the size of the water to almost half of what it is today. This clay bottomed lake has depths down to 8 feet with a few shallower areas and good margins to fish. There is no weed but it does have lovely weeping willows, a few marginal reeds and a good number of flowering lily pads. There is a small island and 18 swims, 2 of which are double swims, on this triangle shaped lake, which was stocked with 80 Kent carp in 1983. Some of these fish reached 30lb+ but, unfortunately, the fishery suffered a high number of deaths in 2003.

Most of the bigger carp where found dead and, to this day, no reason has ever been found, even after tests by various bodies including the Environment Agency. The owner had a small stock pond onsite and 40 carp from this have been introduced and many are now pushing 20lb+. The stock level is today back to 80 fish as well as some pike, large tench, rudd and perch. The commons go to 25lb with mirrors pushing 29lb. Membership numbers are low, at 40 places, and any new member is vetted. A waiting list is in operation.

Rules

3 rods only. No carp sacks, lead core, bait boats or nut baits. Spodding is not permitted. Unhooking mats must be large. Rods must not be left unattended. No litter. Newells closes mid April and re opens on the 1st June each season. The owner lives on site.

Rookfield Pond
Syndicate – West Sussex

Membership and Contact Details

Dave

☎ 07969 661014

www.rockfieldpond.com

Membership Fees

£300

Memberships are restricted to 20 with a waiting list in operation, if necessary, and all members are issued with a photo ID card. The water is open all year although it closes for fishing during spawning. All members must be booked in, so the fishing is from bookings only. Booking of swims is not allowed.

Nearest Main Town

Crawley

Facilities

Carp Size

Rookfield Pond

A few years ago this was almost a dried up, derelict site which was not fishable in any way. Over the last few years, however, extensive work has taken place which has resulted in a complete transformation, from a tip into a secluded and peaceful 2½ acre water which is home to some very good carp. With depths at the dam end going down to 12 feet, the pond offers an average depth of 5 to 6 feet of clay bottom. At the far end there is a weedy shallow area of about 3 to 4 feet which is planned to be a stalking swim. There are only 6 swims, that are all flat and woodchipped, and one is a double. All the swims are on one side of the water and well spaced, with flat, barrow friendly pathways, and all have a bench. In the summer months some areas do get weedy and there are a few lily pads. This lake holds a low number of pike and rudd and around 50 or so commons and mirrors. It's known to hold 3 fish over 30lb, with a good number of back up fish to 25lb and the rest high double figure fish. The lake record is a mirror of just over 32lb.

Members can use the wooden Lodge which has cooking facilities, electricity and a bar-b-que area.

Rules

Barbed hooks only. No lead core, fixed leads or carp sacks. No nuts or maize and boat users must wear a life jacket. There is also the use of a boat if any fish should get snagged. Good sized unhooking mats must be used. Maximum of 3 rods. Night fishing allowed.

we know bivvies inside out

Here at Aqua Products we know our bivvies.

After all we designed and developed the best selling Armo and Pioneer ranges.

We combine research, innovation and design to ensure that every product we make is functional, versatile, durable and comfortable. Only carefully selected performance fabrics and components are used to meet the demands of elite anglers.

Aqua Products... designed from the inside out.

AQUA
Products

Vinnetrow
Syndicate – West Sussex

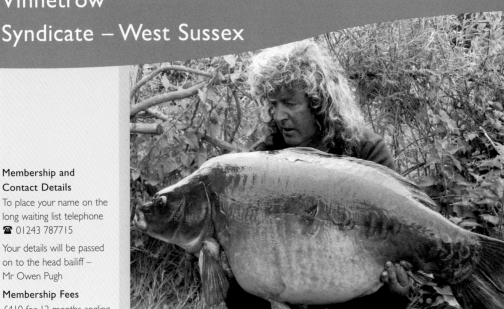

Membership and Contact Details

To place your name on the long waiting list telephone
☎ 01243 787715

Your details will be passed on to the head bailiff – Mr Owen Pugh

Membership Fees

£410 for 12 months angling

Memberships are restricted to 40 tickets and these are always taken very quickly. So, like the angling, getting a membership is more than difficult. Most members are personally known by the onsite bailiff and there is a long waiting list in operation.

Vinnetrow is patrolled on a regular basis and nobody except members are allowed on the banks.

Nearest Main Town

Chichester

Facilities Carp Size

Carp Size

50lb+

Vinnetrow

This specimen carp lake is situated on the entrance to the Southern Leisure Centre Holiday Park. Over the past few years it has produced a string of massive carp, some of which have passed away, only to make way for a new clutch of biggies. It is one of those very special waters that have a knack of producing monsters, being very rich with plant and aquatic life and certainly not overstocked. Vinnetrow was the first water in Sussex to produce a 50lb+ carp. The water is 11 acres in size and has a maximum depth of 7 feet with a lot of shallow areas and, at times, gin clear water. In summer the weed is prolific and the fishing is, without doubt, extremely difficult. On the road bank there are large areas of lily pads in the deep margins, however, fishing on the road bank is not permitted. The total carp stock is around 40 fish, this includes mirrors up to 55lb and a number of commons to 45lb, and it is possible that 4 or 5 different 40lb+ commons are present. This fabulous lake is not for the faint hearted and members go weeks, and sometimes months, without any action. So if it's bites that excite you, then one of the other waters on the complex would be more suitable.

Rules

Barbed hooks only (strictly no barbless). Maximum 3 rods. No bait boats. All other rules are common sense rules. Maximum stay is 72 hours, however members are allowed to book 2 separate full weeks fishing during the year.

I've known of Vinnetrow for many years but it's always been a Gorilla in the mist. Not much information is available online or in brochures. I grew up fishing all of the other venues on the complex, having great fun learning my trade, whilst hearing whispers the whole time about Vinnetrow, but it was still hard to find out information about the fish and its stories. Now that Vinnetrow is protected by its syndicate, the publicity ban that protected its beautiful fish has now been lifted. This gives us all a chance to admire its jewels and also some of its stories.

Currently there is a waiting list in place, so if you would like to fish this venue you need to get your name on the list. There might be a small wait but the wait will be well worth it, I promise!

The lake has about 40-45 fish, mirrors and common. The biggest mirrors are Pecs, which has not been banked for 5 years, and the Half Lin, both sitting comfortably over the 50lb mark, followed by a big black linear that's mid-40 – another rare capture. A beautiful, heavily scaled fish called Scaley (surprisingly) at 43lb+, backed up by Pawprint at 38lb+ and a handful of lower 30lb fish. Not forgetting a smattering of smaller Leney's that hurt the eyes they're so beautiful. Now onto the commons. The Boating Lake common is the biggun, last estimated at 47lb-ish, but uncaught for 6 years. Blunders common, Arnie and the Odog common are all floating just above the 40lb mark. Backed up again by a horde of 30lb commons. A stock that, I'm sure you'll agree, is worth the wait.

When the day comes to wet a line in the mighty Vinnetrow, don't let the impressive stock fool you into a false sense of security. This is for the hard core few and the slightly crazy. The Vinni gods are very cruel! Coupled with the most clued up fish I have ever seen. I call it the Vinni bug, all it takes is your first breath of early morning Vinni air and the bug is inside you! Once you have sampled what Vinni has to offer it's almost impossible to leave. A stunning lake and a host of fish that could take you a lifetime to catch! Many blank nights can be racked up at this venue and many leave fishless for the year but, as I said before, all the waiting is worth it because when you land one of Vinni's A-team all the problems float into the darkness. Vinnetrow can also mimic the crazy people that fish it at times. Multiple catches do happen, but timing is everything with Vinnetrow so homework on moon phases and weather will really help.

In the height of summer the nature and natural life is unrivalled. The water quality of the lakes on the complex is awesome, which has helped to gain the complex the David Bellamy award.

Vinnetrow is a carp fisherman's heaven, there isn't a better place to spend your time. Great people, great venue, awesome fishing.

Hard but awesome!

Westbourne House Lake Syndicate – West Sussex

Membership and Contact Details

Roger Ellis and Steve Burley
☎ 02392 779117 or 07976 841919

info@futurefisheries.co.uk

www.futurefisheries.co.uk

Membership Fees

Membership is set at 55 members and all new applicants have to be recommended and vetted. A waiting list is already in place.

Membership is £450 for the year.

Nearest Main Town

Chichester

Carp Size

Carp Size

43lb+

Westbourne House Lake

The owners of this 30 acre gravel pit have a plan. A plan that only a few could possibly fulfil, I'll explain. Roger Ellis and Steve Burley have a job most carp anglers would die for, they are carp breeders. Roger and Steve are partners in Future Fisheries, which is a CEFAS registered, professionally run fish farm with its own natural carp source. They breed from spawn and have their own unique pure 'Italian' strain carp that have a totally certain genetic parentage. In December 2009 they purchased the water known as Westbourne House, a former tarmac gravel works, and the plan started to take shape. This water already held some very good carp, but numbers were and still are unknown. It is known that at least 20 originals are present in Westbourne but only seven of these originals have been banked since the syndicate was formed, and the best went over 40lb. This lake is a typical, big carp gravel pit with an abundance of plant and aquatic life, including serious amounts of water snails, which shows the quality of the water. Underwater features such as bars, roadways and humps are everywhere amongst 22 natural swims. Depths, in places, go down to 18 feet with shallow areas of 3 to 4 feet, depending on time of year. There are a few marginal reeds and plenty of young bankside cover between the well spaced swims. Entrance to the fishery is via 2 locked security gates and parking is allowed in 2 areas at the top and bottom of lake, via a tarmac and gravel roadway. The longest walk is no more than 100 yards and tackle can be unloaded in many swims.

The water is open 12 months of the year. Pike, tench and roach are present and since the purchase, Future Fisheries have stocked a total of 117 of their own strain of carp. These stockings will take place every winter until the carp population reaches around 250 fish. Future will be hand picking these fish and, to date, fish to just over 20lb have been stocked, the majority of them have been doubles that have already added 5lb to 6lb in weight. For an insight into the stocked fish, have a look at the little beauties on the Future Fisheries website.

Roger and Steve have got this fishery right in every aspect and I have added my name to the waiting list. A proper big carp water where mirrors to 43lb+ and commons to 41lb+ have already been landed.

Rules

Barbed hooks only. 3 rods allowed, 4 in winter. No carp sacks. No lead core. No bait boats. Particles such as hemp and corn are permitted. All other rules are general, common sense rules.

Woodmere Pool
Syndicate – West Sussex

Membership and Contact Details

Mr John Rice

☎ 01273 834165

Membership Fees

Memberships run from 1st April each year with the fishery closed for fishing on the 14th March until 1st May. All potential new members are vetted.

£300 plus a joining fee of £100 for the first season.

Nearest Main Town

Horsham

Facilities

Carp Size

28lb+

Woodmere Pool

The Sussex Carp Conservation Group is a small band of carpers that was formed in 1970. They have their own water, which is only fishable to paid-up members that have been invited to join. Membership is limited to just 22. Woodmere Pool is set in rural surroundings and covers just over 3 acres. There are 24 spacious swims that all have plenty of bankside cover between them. The pool was manmade way back in the 1800's and has 2 small islands and 1 large island. A clay and flat bottomed water with depths to an average of 4 feet, this peaceful pool has no weed and holds mirrors to 28lb+ and the Woodmere commons go up to 26lb. It also contains rudd and a few pike.

Rules

3 rods only. No carp sacks or lead core. No fires, litter or unattended rods. No nut baits. All other rules are common sense rules. Fisheries own mats, slings and nets must be used, all provided by SCCG.

Maximum stay in any one swim is 7 days with no restrictions of time spent at the water.

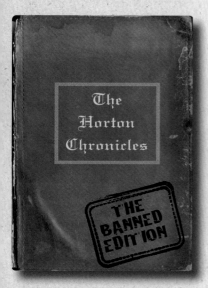
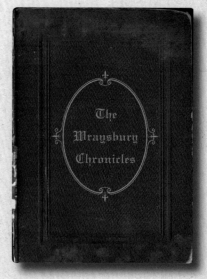

Particle Baits or Boilies?

by Clive Williams

I have always loved fishing with particles, for me it's a more natural way for the carp to feed, grubbing about on the bottom in amongst all the debris and silt. In general most particles are smaller than your average size boilie and the seed types tend to be dark in colour and disappear into the makeup of the lake bed, making them much harder for the fish to actually see. Carp do not spend their time picking up natural food items like bloodworm in ones and twos, they bury their heads and trough around in the silt, sending all types of muck flying about as they search the area for the grub they know is there. Boilies are sometimes picked up one at a time, particularly on clear waters where the carp can, if needed, feed by sight.

I have used particles at all times of the year, including the winter. When I was a bailiff at Les Quis we used to do winter trips when the fishery was closed, to carry out fishery chores. Of course, these chores included getting the rods out and we always fished with small amounts of hemp and tiger nuts, with a couple of nuts on the rig, and we caught loads. I would go as far as to say that they out fished any rod on a boilie so in the end we banned boilies amongst ourselves.

The most important aspect of using particles is, without doubt, the preparation of your chosen bait. This can be confusing as the choice of particles is very wide so, below, I have listed a few of the most widely used baits, ones I have used myself over the years, and I have also given a cooking and soak time for each particle which should be carried out before any use.

Tiger Nuts

One of the best ever carp baits, especially as it tends to keep the nuisance fish away as well. Soak for at least 24 hours then cook for at least 30 minutes or until they are soft enough to easily crush with your teeth. The outer shell should be nice and smooth and not wrinkly.

If tigers are cooked 3 times it brings out the natural sugars in them and they taste even better and more crunchy. Leave to cool before each cook.

Chick Peas

Another very visual bait good in the right water. Can be dyed pink or red with ease. Soak for at least 12 hours. Cook for at least 30 minutes or until finger squashable.

Hemp Seed

The smell of cooked hemp makes me want to go fishing. Irresistible to most cyprinids and a seed that is easily lost in the depths of any lake making carp uproot the lake bed in search of them. Works well mixed with most baits. Soak for at least 24 hours. Cook for at least 30 minutes or until the seeds split to reveal the white kernels.

Red Kidney Beans

A large and buoyant bean which is good in a silty situation. Soak for at least 12 hours then cook for no less than 30 minutes.

Soya Beans

Like sweetcorn, bright yellow in colour when cooked so they show up well on any bottom. One of the smallest beans, they have very little flavour, but do work well with hemp. Soak for at least 12 hours then cook for at least 30 minutes or until softish.

French Maize

I have no idea why carp love this cheap bait, but they do. It has almost no taste or smell and I can only assume that it is like corn, very visual and mixes well with most other particles and it can also be dyed. Soak for at least 24 hours. Cook for at least 30 minutes or when softish between your teeth.

Maple Peas

These small, brown peas have a distinctive taste, with a high oil content. A heavy bait that works well in silt and coloured water, where the carp feed by smell. Soak for at least 12 hours. Cook for at least 30 minutes or until hookable. Works very well when fished with hemp or tares.

Tares

Bigger than hemp but just as strong in smell. They sink well in silt and work well with most particles. Soak for at least 12 hours. Cook for at least 30 minutes.

Groats

A handy bait to take dry on long trips, as there is no need to cook them, they just need to be soaked for up to 48 hours. A small bait that mixes well with other small seeds and gives off a lovely, milky slick.

Wheat

Another good one to take on long trips as a backup, in case you have a result and use your cooked bait quickly. It is lightweight and sits on weed. Cook for 20 to 30 minutes then leave to soak in hot water.

Particle Baits or Boilies?

by Clive Williams

Sunflower Hearts

These are the seed without the husk. Oil packed and a high energy food, carp love 'em! No need to cook. Look to buy bakery grade hearts which are not cheap.

Soak for 48 hours in boiling water and cover. Another good one on any long trip as you can bring them home if not used.

Aniseed Party Mix

A great one to add to any mix of particles with a great smell. Another one that does not need cooking, just scald or bring to the boil and leave in the hot water. Works with most others particles and good in silt. Gets the carp searching hard.

Notes

Although I have never found it necessary to add any flavours or additives to my particles, some can give the bait that little edge. Those that are known to work well are brown sugar, salt, liquid betaine and sweeteners.

To reduce cooking times use a pressure cooker but always check that they are cooked to be soft enough to eat yourself. Remember, if particles are not prepared correctly they can be dangerous to fish.

If I could only ever fish with boilies or particles again I know what I would choose. Watch the bottom get ripped up.

County Rivers

The Sussex rivers, like a lot of the UK's rivers, are in some cases almost untapped for carp, due to the popularity of stillwater carping and the great number of day ticket venues now available.

Our rivers, it is fair to say, have been left alone by all except a small number of hardy souls who love the solitude that river carping gives. Unlike the information gained from making just one phone call to a commercial fishery, obtaining info on our rivers was a different kettle of fish (excuse the pun). It was, and is, much harder to come by simply because of a lack of anglers to ask. Needless to say that those that were "in the know" also wanted to keep that information to themselves after years of their own hard work, and rightly so.

This section is a guide to the clubs that control various stretches of river along The Adur, The Arun, The Ouse and both the Eastern and Western Rother. All of these rivers hold carp, some small, some big and some difficult to find, but they are there all right. If it's a real challenge that excites you then the rivers could just surprise and delight you. Happy hunting!

The River Adur

The River Adur

The Adur is just one of the rivers that drain our county. It begins life as two separate branches, the western Adur and the eastern Adur, which meet just west of the town of Henfield. This waterway was once navigable by large vessels as far up as Steyning but over time the river valley became silted up and boat traffic stopped.

The western arm is about 7½ miles long and rises at Slinfold. From here it flows around Coolham and through the village of Shipley, where it is met by the Lancing Brook before flowing on to Knepp Castle and West Grinstead. From here the arm then flows south towards Henfield, where it meets the eastern arm.

The eastern arm of the Adur starts its life at Ditchling Common where it winds its way around the north of Burgess Hill and westwards towards the village of Twineham where it is fed by the Bolney stream. From here it travels to Shermanbury to be fed by the Cowfold stream before joining up with the western arm at Bines Green. From there it goes through Upper Beeding and Bramber and on through a gap in the south downs near Lancing. Here it is met by the last stream, the Ladywell. From here the river continues onto the English Channel at Shoreham-by-sea. The eastern arm is approximately 12 miles long, the tidal stretch is about 9 miles and extends as far north as Bines Bridge. There are 23 bridges from the mouth of the river at Shoreham harbour. The tidal limit on the eastern section is the Shermanbury foot bridge.

Clubs who control stretches of this river are as follows:

Pulborough Angling Society

The society controls approximately 3 miles of tidal water from Stretham Bridge, near Small Dole, downstream to Bramber. The width of the river is about 25 metres and depths are varied. The club allow night fishing for 2 rods only. This section of the Adur holds a large head of bream as well as other species including sea trout, perch, roach, chub, pike and carp into double figures. The club's largest known Adur carp is just over 20lbs. Tidal time at Stretham is 2 hours after high tide at Shoreham. Car parking nearby is not easy.

Hassocks & District Angling Society

The Hassocks DAS have a section of upper, non-tidal river in the area of the village of Twineham. This is a narrow stretch which offers good fishing for bream, roach, chub, perch and pike. The society report very few catches of carp, although they are almost certainly present, but numbers and sizes are not known. Night fishing is allowed for 2 rods until 1st October when a 3rd rod is permitted. There is parking nearby.

Henfield & District Angling Society

This angling society has various stretches of the Adur totalling 14 miles. This includes both tidal and non-tidal parts of the river from Stretham Bridge, which is a fast flowing section, right up to the non-tidal area around Wineham on the eastern arm. They control some known good carp areas such as the fork where the western arm joins up with the main river. Also under their control is the downstream section around the Bines Bridge area. These stretches contain many good fish including big bream, chub and both mirror and common carp. The society's records show that mirrors over 25lb have been landed around the Bines area and possibly the biggest common from any Sussex river when Joe Raczkowski banked a fish weighing 36lb 8oz from the fork section, this record has stood since 2005. Night fishing is allowed.

River Adur Conservation Society

The River Adur has its own conservation society (RACS) which was formed in July 2007 with the aim of improving the river and its tributaries. They work with all fishing clubs to be successful in its aims and have a strong voice for the whole river. New members are welcome. See website. www.sussex-adur.org.uk

The River Adur

by Joe Raczkowski

The River Adur flows through West Sussex. This river is part tidal and part non-tidal due to several weirs along its length. The lower part of the river is brackish with no features and the flow is fast with the incoming tides. Above the weirs the flow is slow, and in the summer this upper region, above the weirs, the water is clear but very weedy, this is ideal for easy fish location and stalking with float tackle, or using floating crust or a dog biscuit.

There are places where you can fish using standard ledger gear, if you wish to fish at night. My favourite method is floating crust as you can pick up individual large carp. I pointed out a good holding spot to Andy Little once but although he missed a 30lb fish, he did land a 28lb common carp on a dog biscuit.

There is a fork in the river where the river splits into two sections, here the water level can change very dramatically from a 4.2 to a 7 metre tide. At low water it's shallow and muddy but still has depths of four or five feet.

The Adur is a river that is very under fished for carp. I have fished the River Adur for carp for over thirty years and I believe it to be one of the best rivers for carp fishing that I know. I have caught many, many fish of all different sizes, commons and mirrors but mainly doubles with some twenty plus fish and a few thirties. I have three very good friends that are very well known carp anglers that also have had fish to thirty pounds from the Adur.

I remember one of my sessions, where I arrived at the river late one afternoon at low tide with the intention to fish all night, as high tide was due at about 12.30. I had plenty of time to do some water craft before setting up my tackle. I looked along the river banks where I intended to fish, to see if there were any heart shaped marks in the mud of the river bank, which is a sign of bream feeding in the area. If there are I will move well away as I don't want to be up all night catching bream. There were signs of bream so I moved up river to a spot I had fished many times, where there is a small eddy under my feet with a reed bed to my left. It was going to be a big tide so I sheltered my bait and line from any debris coming up and down with the tide.

I set up a standard combi-link with an inch stripped back for a popped up tutti-frutti boilie, as fishmeal will bring in the eels. I laid my rig into position on the muddy bank, with a dozen boilies cut in half to stop them rolling around in the flow, then I put on a back lead. My second rod was fished near the far bank with a PVA bag. With everything set, I sat and waited for the tide to come in. One very important safety tip is to make sure you set up high on the bank so when the tide comes in, you and your tackle are safe and do not get wet.

While waiting for the tide I noticed two more anglers setting up just down the river from me. They put a lot of ground bait into the river so I think they must be going to fish for Bream.

Just after darkness the Mullet arrived in large numbers with the turn of the tide. I know the carp will be following just behind them up river hopefully on the feed. Up to an hour before high tide I was just getting line bites, when suddenly my alarm screamed off. I jumped up and grabbed my rod just as it was being pulled off the rod rest. It felt like a big fish. I struggled to keep the fish in front of me but couldn't, it seemed to have a mind of its own and raced off against the flow so all I could do was to follow it. In the excitement I left my torch behind so I stumbled along the uneven river bank. I tried hard to get the fish back in my own swim as my landing net and unhooking mat were there.

I was getting closer and closer to the anglers I saw earlier. I apologised for disturbing them but was still unable to get the fish back to my own swim, even though it was tiring and slowing down by me applying more pressure. Finally getting the fish under control, I played it under my rod for five to ten minutes then the fish suddenly came to the surface and I could just see it in the dark.

I called to the other anglers and asked if they could help me by lending me a torch and landing net. One grabbed a net, the other a torch and I asked him not to shine it directly on the fish. I played it until it was right under our bank, then I saw it in full for the first time, it was massive. I tried to keep calm until I saw the size of their 24 inch pan net. I said it wouldn't be big enough and after a few attempts at netting it, I asked one of them (I found out his name was Alex) if he would get my net from my swim. He ran off to get it but I couldn't understand why he took so long. The carp was rolling and splashing in front of me and I had visions of losing the fish. At last Alex arrived back with my net. I took it from him and netted the fish in one go. She was mine. Apparently Alex ran right past my swim, God knows how far.

Keeping the netted fish in the water I ran back to get my unhooking mat, scales, weigh sling and camera. Upon my return I picked up the fish and my thoughts were 30lb plus, her weight was 36lb 3oz. It was an extremely long common and in perfect condition. Not only was it the river record but also my P.B. for the Adur, so I was over the moon with my catch. After returning the fish to the river I sat down with Alex and Brian for a cup of tea when it dawned on me my second rod was still out. I ran back to my swim quickly, lucky enough my rod was still there - lucky me. I packed up my tackle, said goodbye to my two new friends and drove home with a big grin on my face.

The River Arun

The River Arun

This river starts its life in the St. Leonards Forest area of Horsham where the source is a series of small streams known locally as ghylls. Around 2 miles from the source is the first stretch that is known to hold some carp. The Kerves Lane area was once controlled by Horsham & District AA and in the early eighties some fish escaped from a private pond after flooding and are thought to still be present in this small, deep section, although sizes and numbers are unknown. This small stretch is now on land open to the public. After running through the south of Horsham, the river is joined by the locally known Red River which is born from the overflow of Warnham Mill Pond. From here is a narrow section of water which winds its way through open countryside past the villages of Broadbridge Heath and Rapkyns (unfished and barbel present) and on to Rudgwick and Bucks Green where it heads south towards the village of Billingshurst and the secluded Lee Place section, which is known to hold carp to over 25lb. Just downstream of Lee Place is the last stretch of non-tidal water at Pallingham Quay Farm, a distance of about 7½ miles from source. From here the river becomes tidal, fast flowing and deep where it widens at Pythingdean. It then runs under the A283 at Stopham where it is joined by the western River Rother at the famous Stopham Bridge, an area known to hold some big carp. From Stopham it winds its way through Pulborough and south towards Arundel where the river gets wider (about 20 to 30 metres) and faster, especially around the Monarchs Way section at Arundel, and on to Littlehampton Harbour to spill out into the English Channel, a stretch of approximately just over 25 miles, a few bridges, 5 locks and untold carp.

Clubs who control stretches of this river are:

Horsham & District Angling Association

Horsham DAA control 4 miles of the non-tidal river at Lee Place, Billingshurst. It is a secluded section where night fishing is allowed with 2 rods only. There are lots of species present, including large chub, roach, dace and a good number of double figure carp, and it has produced a mirror of just over 25lb. There is no weed and plenty of bankside cover, and also nearby car parking.

Billingshurst Angling Society

This club shares the Lee Place section with Horsham & DAA. The club record for carp in this area is 23lb. The upper stretch from Lording Lock to Newbridge is a varied non-tidal section where carp show on a regular basis well into double figures. This is a deep section with many gliding bends and aquaducts. 2 rods only. There is good parking at a number of points close to the river.

Rother Angling Club

The club has 2 sections of tidal water near the village of Pulborough. A half mile stretch upstream on the west bank from Greatham Bridge, which is known to hold carp well into 20lb. There is car parking by the bridge.

They also control an exclusive 1 mile stretch upstream from Stopham Bridge. This is an area designated as a Site of Special Scientific Interest so night fishing is not permitted. Sizes of carp are unknown but they are present.

Pulborough Angling Society

This society controls 3 miles of tidal river at Greatham, Parham, Washingham, Stopham and Hardham. The area around Greatham has depths that go to over 12 feet in places and contains various species that include roach, chub, perch, pike, bream as well as mullet and sea trout. It is also known to hold a few carp to over 30lb. Night fishing is allowed. Tide time at Greatham is 3 hours after tide at Littlehampton.

Worthing & District Piscatorial Society

The society leases several miles of deep, fast flowing water. One fishery is in beautiful countryside and runs for 1½ miles from the B2139 at Houghton Bridge upstream to Bury. Access is to the west bank only.

A second stretch runs from Bury to Timberley Farm. Fishing access is 300 yards upstream of Bury Ferry to the fork at the northern end of Timberley Farm. Night fishing is allowed on both these sections, which contain carp to over 20lb and a good stock of double figure fish.

The third section runs from Arundel Bridge to South Stoke. A wide, fast flowing section that is weed free and known to be home to a small amount of good sized carp. Night fishing is allowed. Access to the west bank only.

CEMEX Angling

CEMEX angling control the fishing on 2000 metres of one bank south of Pulborough village. This tidal stretch holds mirrors to 24lb and commons over 20lb. There is a nearby car park and night fishing is allowed. 2 rods only.

Hassocks & District Angling Society

This club has a small, exclusive stretch of the Arun near to Stopham Bridge at Pulborough. Approximately 500 yards of tidal bank on the station side, which can be fished at night. 2 rods are allowed until October, when a third may be used. This stretch has produced carp to over 30lb.

Petworth & Bognor Angling Club

This club has one of the most varied sections of the Arun at Watersfield. A 1 mile tidal stretch with deep, lazy bends and fast flowing shallow areas. It has a reputation for shoals of big bream and many other species, including the occasional large carp well over 20lb. The mid section has marginal reeds and high tide is 2½ hours from Littlehampton's tide. There is easy access from the car park, night fishing is not allowed. 2 rods only.

The River Arun

Joining details of the clubs listed are in the club section apart from:

Rudgwick Angling Society

Although this is a Sussex club it has no listing in the club section because all of its stillwaters are in Surrey, however it does have a stretch of the River Arun. It is a non profit making, small club based in the village of Rudgwick with around 150 members, and was established in 1932. The club's Arun stretch is on the non-tidal upper river around Gibbons Mill and Clemsfold and is known to hold a number of carp in the 10lb to 13lb range. Night fishing is allowed. 2 rods only.

Memberships / Joining Fees

Contact Mr. George Wingate

☎ 01798 873412

Adult £30

OAP/Disabled/Junior £10

Husband/wife and 2 children £30

> No matter where you are, or what you catch, the most important elements are to tread lightly, enjoy your angling and have fun along the way
>
> Gaz Fareham

The phone rings, it's old school carper Clive Williams, the very bloke who had a part in setting me off on this crazy carp fishing adventure around 25 years ago. His legendary C.A.A regional drinkathon meetings at Horsham F.C helped spark the carp fishing bug within me, but at the time I didn't have a clue as to the style of fishing that would absorb most of my bank tramping in the last 12 years or so. Now I know!

Picture this……

Clive: I'm doing a book on Sussex carping and I've got your name down for the River Arun chapter.

Me: No chance mate, it's one of my favourite places.

Clive: Well if you don't do it, I will get someone else to blow it all out of the water!

Me: err … I will talk to my brother! A day later I'd decided a good stroke had been pulled and I'd write it.

So how do you write an interesting chapter without blowing the river out of the water? Easy really, because it's challenging enough as it is without giving away coordinates to my favourite spots…just as long as you find it interesting.

Now, I'm not going to follow the usual path of a river article here, i.e. peace and solitude etc, but in the late nineties our carping took a turn for the better. That turn was to decide that chasing big, stupidly named (circus) carp wasn't for us and big, wild untapped venues seemed the more appealing places to go to. Be it un-fished lakes, reservoirs or rivers, that's where we were going to fish. After all, who wants to catch a fish called Clive or Dave or….the list goes on!

So, why the Arun? Well, for a start it was my local river. Secondly, I'd fished it for small stuff all my fishing life and knew about it being one of the fastest tidal rivers in England. The main reason, though, came about through fishing some lakes around my home town of Horsham with my brother James and good friends Richard Patrick and Gary Smart. Whilst spending time at one such lake, we noticed how many carp were actually escaping into the river, below which, of course is the River Arun.

The River Arun

by Andrew Deeley

Around the same time Rich and I used to fish with sticks, Huckleberry Finn style, for a laugh. One evening, as well as the usual 8-9 different species, something else turned up out of the browny blue. The stick bent over and after a good little scrap, up popped a carp! In total, in that short evening stick contest, we went on to catch around 30 small but beautiful mirror carp up to about a pound. Never having caught any from the river before, we wondered where on earth they had come from. It transpired that around 300 had 'spilled' from an estate lake stock pond that adjoined the river. That trip, as well as the lake escapees, made me wonder just how many carp there might be in the river and whether it was worth fishing it? Of course it was.

Fast forward to the following close season and we looked at a few spots on the non-tidal down to the last weir 'just above' Pulborough. Note to self: using the invading barbel crowd's lingo is not big and sounds stupid. . . Back to the carping! The whole upper river didn't really look that carpy and anyway, I could imagine all the carp being slowly washed down river in the heavy flash floods that the Arun is renowned for. So, where to start?

The tidal river must be something over 15 miles long and to the untrained eye, it does resemble a raging torrent of chocolate sometimes. However, it is so varied throughout its length that many areas all the way to the estuary are capable of holding carp. There are stacks of features including big depth and type of bottom variations. You can have a 200 metre section of weedy gravel 2 feet deep giving way to 15 feet deep silty runs. Other areas have mud flats rising to the surface as well as back channels and ditches that the fish get into, amongst many other features. It was the tidal where we finally decided to concentrate our fishing.

Now, I mentioned the carp that swam out of the Horsham lakes. It soon transpired that carp had escaped from various other lakes along the Arun/Rother system as well. Add in the odd rumoured stocking by the old National Rivers Authority and it all added up to a very varied stock of carp. I think my friends and I have still only scratched the surface of the different strains some 10 years after starting our campaign. What I like about having so many different strains of carp is that it adds weight to the element of the unknown biggie. For some people, that extra weight might be ounces or the lack of belief that the river will do something special. For me, it could be ten or twenty pounds bigger due to the strain washed in, or even bred from two different escapees. Alternatively, it could just be a twenty.

Looking back to our first trip, we had decided to try an area on the upper tidal to find our feet with the place. The tide variation still came up 3-4 feet on average so it was still tricky, but the current isn't as bad and the flotsam is nowhere near the levels seen further down. We baited for a good 2 weeks before fishing with a whole mix of bait, but mainly maize and boilies. The first night was electric. I remember sitting there wondering if I had any fish within a mile of me but I needn't have doubted it as my alarm went into meltdown less than an hour later. It was only a common of about 10lb but a good start none the less. Rich, fishing just round the next bend, managed an 8lb bream and had all his bait eaten. Not by fish but a group of cows that spent the whole night trying to stick their heads under his brolly to lick his face! After that session we baited hard but action was sporadic. The highlight was a 27.10lb sparsely scaled mirror but, strangely, I caught it away from the bait on a high attract bait. What did this mean? Well, we came to the conclusion that we were fishing a 'passing' through spot. There wasn't enough cover for the fish to hold up in and by baiting heavily whilst fishing, we were lessening our chances of a pick up. Back to the drawing board.

Later, James caught a nice mirror the first night in a new spot. It was the kind of spot that just looked more carpy. You know the type of stuff carp like…. trees in the water, weed, rushes and pads etc. That was one part of the huge Arun jigsaw that the carp still have most of the pieces of, somewhere down in their mysterious river. Since then we have found that you need to fish areas where the carp are happy to hold up - fish their home if you like. You can bait the hell out of some areas but will you be there when they come through? As a part time bank tramp……..quite possibly.

The new area we had located went from strength to strength, although it required stacks of bait. The resident bream must have got through a lot, as did the tench and chub, but surely out of some 500-600kg of bait over a spell of around two and a half months, there was plenty left for the carp. After fishing the same area for so long, patterns began to emerge with the tide. For a start, different strains (and sizes) of fish would show up depending on the

moon phase and tide. I doubt it was one group of carp pushing another out, it was more likely that catching a few of each group of carp that turned up in our swims would spook them off. It didn't really matter, though, because in turn each group would be replaced by a tide conveyor belt of other carp. It could also be the case that the various pods of carp are so in tune with their natural food and tidal range that they only need to visit your spots at certain times of year. Both ways, it all started to seem a bit easier, this River Arun adventure. One week a load of commons would turn up. Next week a few mirrors, and so on, culminating in a couple of those heavy, sparsely scaled mirrors of the same strain, one night on one of the biggest tides of the year. It may be coincidence with the big tide, but the mosquitoes were almost the size of mini bats that night, constantly trying to eat you. So is it the hatch that causes the catch or the baiting pyramid effect? I doubt that either are the be all and end all, but both are small chunks in the Arun carp jigsaw. My theory for all these different fish turning up in tide phase rotation is probably more of a factor.

Different groups of fish could have home areas at different times of the year. Each year is unique, but they drift up and down on the tide with little effort, browsing on all manner of stuff. If the tide brings them to your area and they have enough food, they will either stay put because they are comfortable, or they won't drift back down so far due to wasting tide travelling time eating, and will repeatedly come back. For most carp to be comfortable to hold up in the area, they need some refuge from the current, otherwise they would have to eat constantly. Any 's' bends, where they can move from one side to the other depending on which way the flow is travelling, are usually handy spots. Sharp right/left angle bends after a long straight will also hold fish. Very large trees in the water block flow and hold food. Finally, gravel humps and mud flats on the down side of the flow are worth looking at, especially if they are mid-river and are covered in weed.

Talking of tides again, we have found the night tide ten times better than the day tide. Why? I'm not totally sure but it may be that a lot of the carp's food filter feeds off the tide and is susceptible to light levels. The worms and mussels might not come out of the silt so much. Maybe the carp feel

The River Arun

by Andrew Deeley

more comfortable at night due to light levels and that the heavy tackle is too obvious in the day. We haven't found the answers to those questions yet, and maybe never will. Having said that, one theory that could be applied to the bite time on the Arun is that, on other rivers we have fished that have much clearer water clarity, the carp have been predominantly sight feeders. Bright pop ups fished off the lead have been the winning method during the day until dusk, when the bites nearly always dry up. Maybe, due to the chocolate coloured nature of the tidal Arun, a big smelly bottom bait is more likely to be found than a little chod style pop up. We have tried all sorts of combinations but still the night tide rules the bites.

With the tackle and bait, it's down to the individual but it needs to be super strong! I have been flat rodded and busted up on 20lb hook links by several unknown, animal fish and had 15lb big game line busted after changing from 30lb braid. Braid is my line of choice, normally, but it seems to collect all manner of rubbish when fishing this river. There are massive pike and sea trout in the river and some of the unknown, unstoppable monsters could have been those species before I stopped taking chances. There is also at least one catfish in the river. My mate Gary saw it at a culvert near the trout lake in Arundel. Suffice to say it was sat there with its mouth open hoping for a trout to just plop in. I want to add something here to the monster alien fish bit. I caught a good size ghostie many years ago. A few years later, I spoke to two people separately that both claimed to have seen a ghost carp of around 40lb. They had never crossed paths either, which gives the sightings some credence. I wouldn't normally doubt it, but a 40lb albeit plastic carp in the Arun?!! All that talk of monsters reminded me of something else. If anyone manages to land one of the occasional seals that run up the river, could they please let me know as I am unsure as to whether Klinik should be applied and how long a pole the bottle should be attached to! Back to the real carp....

Since losing some very strong fish, I've usually fished 25lb braided hook links, size 2 or 3 hooks with the rods in the air to avoid the flotsam. That size of hook sounds excessive but when you have had size 4's opened straight, it makes sense. The close in rods can have 2 ounce back leads fished off the rod tips, paper clip style, with 4-8oz main leads. Far bank rods require much bigger weights (or even two 4 ounce watch or grippers, due to the greater surface area), but the flotsam can get real bad, making the river unfishable at times. Think 20 metre long rafts of seaweed and rushes, fences and dead animals and you're half way there. The further down you go, the worse it gets and as it behaves like a female river - temperamental, sometimes moody but very satisfying periodically, what goes down must come back up...and go down again twice a day, every day. Bait is a personal thing, really, and much depends on the spot, how much time you have to bait it and type of bait you want to use. As a general rule, though, it really is beneficial to bait up extensively and still use plenty when you are fishing. With the tide constantly changing, it does help to have attraction drifting down, up or down. Get my drift? Oils, glugs, pellets and ground bait are all good for this. Short of giving out free hand grenades, I think that's plenty enough on the tactics.

So what does the future hold for this great river, in my opinion Sussex's River Severn. Well, in recent times the otter releasing schemes have done their bit and I have seen signs of these carp munchers about. Not a good thing when the biggies are few and far between. There has also been a fair few Borat lookalikes trying their luck although, at the moment, their methods are fairly crude. More and more fixed lines are appearing with time, so if you're going to give it a crack, remain vigilant. I believe that only a very small percentage of anglers, regardless of where they come from, want to steal fish for a fast buck, or fancy making a nice carp stew. I also believe a good proportion of carp anglers seem decent enough folk who care about the waters they fish and I am sure those who choose to fish the Arun in the future will look after the river in these tough times. If you end up loving fishing on the Arun as much as my brother and I, we will rest easy knowing there are more safe pairs of hands looking out for the place. In the absence of the EA, let's call it self policing... especially if you see anyone in a mankini. No citizen's arrests, though, as it could well be the EA or the police off duty, wearing one of those! I hope I am not giving Nash or Fox any idea's here, as Realtree mankini's would not look good. Some people will go to any length when it comes to camo though..... or should that be commando? Let's face it, if you can buy a camo toilet roll holder or a camo torch, anything is possible.

The other thing I have worried about in the past is unscrupulous lake owners. There are a fair few in Sussex, and it was the main reason for initially being apprehensive about writing this. Well, they can try but maybe it's a bit too hard for mainly double figure fish that carry parasites. Yes... if any dodgy lake owners are reading this, the parasites are why I am told the N.R.A dumped a load of carp in there in the first place. For the genuine carpers out there that are thinking of having a fish on the river, please dry your nets before taking them elsewhere.

Fast forward to the current situation on the river and there certainly seems to be less fish in the river. That's if bites are anything to go by. For sure it has the possibility to do another 30lb fish and maybe much bigger, however, they are very, very rare, but maybe one day.. hopefully sometime soon......

If you are driven solely by catching one large fish after another, then the Arun isn't for you. They are mainly doubles, with the odd twenty. If, on the other hand, you like the buzz of not knowing what's going to happen next then all credit to you and good luck. You will love it and may get a really good, wild carp without a stupid name.

Finally, I just want to bring up those small stick caught carp again, that partly started my Arun fishing mission. Two summers ago we started catching a load of mirrors of 8-13lb that looked familiar. This summer we had several of those mirrors in a couple of trips that were a bit bigger. I believe them to be those very same carp and they had made it all the way down from Horsham, some 10 years later. How big are they going to get in the future? Who knows, but periodically I intend to carry on my lifelong Arun fishing mission to find out.

By writing this, I have reminisced, remembered and recharged my Arun battery for next season. I have also noticed how many question marks I have employed. That's because the Arun is still a great mystery to me and probably always will be. I am glad my friends and I chose this wild style of carping in the ever maddening carp circus. Maybe if you're up for a proper fishing challenge, I will see you down there some time.

Cheers for now and enjoy it no matter what ends up in your landing net... seals permitting!

The River Ouse

The River Ouse

The River Ouse runs for approximately 42 miles, of which 9 miles from Newhaven to Barcombe is tidal. It rises at Bells Farm near the village of Lower Beeding and runs eastwards across open farmland, under the Ouse Valley viaduct, south of Ardingly Reservoir, before pushing into the east of the county around Sheffield Park and the Bluebell Railway. From here it travels south under the A272 at Newick and on to Sharpsbridge and Barcombe Mills, where it is joined by many small tributaries. At Hamsey it forms a loop around Hamsey Island before flowing through the town of Lewes, an area that has produced carp to over 30lb. From here it passes under the A27 and on towards the English Channel passing Southease, Deans Farm and Piddinghoe to empty into the sea at Newhaven.

Clubs who control stretches of this river are as follows.

Ouse Angling Preservation Society

This society was formed in 1875 and gives access to several miles of fishing north of Lewes, where it has a sharing agreement with Copthorne DAS. The Ouse APS stretches include the tidal Hamsey Cut and up to the non-tidal Barcombe Mills. This lower section has produced a number of good sized carp, including commons to over 34lb. North of Barcombe OAPS control areas around the Anchor Inn and Browns Farm. Day tickets are available on both of these stretches of river. The societies newsletter in 2010 claims that a huge common was seen in the upper tidal section, a fish said to be in the mid 40lb region. The society's water has also produced a grass carp of 29lb. Night fishing is not allowed on OAPS controlled stretches. 2 rods only.

As this society is not listed elsewhere in this book joining details are as follows:

Fees

Adult season ticket £68. Senior £34. Under 19 years £17.
Adult winter tickets from 1st November £42.
Under 13 years old free when with an adult member.

Contacts

Permits are available from all the local tackle shops or via post from the membership secretary.

14 The Martlets, Mill Lane, South Chailey, Sussex BN8 4QG.

Call 01273 891312 in the first instance.

Website www.ouseaps.co.uk

Copthorne & District Angling Society

Copthorne has a sharing agreement with The Ouse Angling Preservation Society but does have an exclusive stretch where they allow night fishing. This is about 4 miles of water from Goldsbridge on the A272 down to the Anchor Inn where the river is slow moving. Carp and bream are predominant in this area. 2 rods only.

Hassocks & District Angling Society

This society fishes a stretch of tidal river at Hamsey, just outside Lewes, which is bisected by a weir. Above the weir is a known area for carp. Night fishing is allowed and a 3rd rod may be used after the 18th of November. This society's water has produced commons to over 34lb.

Haywards Heath & District Angling Society

The society has access to both banks of the picturesque Lindfield stretch, down to East Mascalls Bridge, which includes a stretch going through Paxhill golf course. This area is slow and wide and has good access. It contains all the usual species and the occasional large carp. Depths vary from 4 feet to a few deeper parts due to a flood relief channel. After leaving East Mascalls, the river runs through Henfield Wood and down to the Sloop Lane area. This stretch is said to fish well all season and holds a large variety of quality fish, including some carp. Around the Fletching area the society controls about a mile of upstream water that is under fished. Slow moving and 5 to 6 feet deep, it is described as a prime area for holding large carp. The society's last stretch meanders upstream for about a mile from the Goldsbridge (A272). An average depth of 4 feet can be found in this slow moving area and both commons and mirrors into double figures have been caught from this part of the river. Night fishing is allowed. 2 rods only.

Seaford Angling Club

The club controls a stretch around the Hamsey area, which is tidal and known to hold good sized carp. Night fishing is allowed. 2 rods only.

Details of the clubs listed can be found in the club section.

Bait up your swim little and often
Mick Nolan

The Rother (Eastern)

The Rother (Eastern)

The Eastern Rother is 35 miles long and spills into the English Channel at Rye and Camber Sands. Going upstream towards Wittersham (Kent) it crosses into Kent around the B2082 Wittersham Road. From here it flows west to Maytham Wharf where, for about 1 mile, it re-enters East Sussex. The Potmans Channel in this area has produced some large carp. At New Barn it becomes the border between the two counties for approximately 4 miles and, uniquely, you could actually hook a carp on the far Kent margin and land it in Sussex. It re-enters Sussex west of Bodiam Castle, before meandering its way to Robertsbridge, Etchingham and Witherenden Hill where it twists and turns all the way to Wellbook and on to the source near Rotherfield. The river is tidal up to the large Iden lock which takes over its flow for a short distance of about 4 miles.

Clubs who control stretches of this river are as follows:

Rother Fishery Association

This is not a fishing club, as individual memberships are not available. Only clubs can join at a fee of £3.25 per angler. The RFA was set up in 1872 by a group of local landowners to regulate the fishing on the river. As time progressed the RFA developed into a management organisation by renting stretches from the landowners and controlling the fishing, which is just what they do today. In total, some 4000 anglers have access through their clubs to RFA waters. The RFA control 13 miles of different stretches from the narrow, shallow areas around Robertsbridge to the Wittersham area, where the river becomes much wider and deeper. The lower reaches are, in places, 35 to 40 meters wide with depths to 10 feet. The upper sections are said to be unlikely areas to hold carp, although a few fish have been landed at Newenden where the river starts to get deeper and wider. The lower end of the Rother is the area for the carp, which have been landed to over 34lb. It has what is described as a healthy stock of carp, both mirrors and commons, and a lot of 20lb+ fish. Other species include the usual coarse fish. Clubs from any county can join the RFA so these waters are shared with many clubs including some based in Sussex.

These clubs are:

Clive Vale Angling Club

Crowborough & District Anglers Association

Dorset Arms Angling Club

Hastings, Bexhill & District Angling Association
The Hastings club controls two stretches that are exclusive to club members.

Above Bodiam the river is quite narrow and said to hold few carp. The clubs lower section is 25 yards wide with depths down to 10 feet and is known to hold carp to 20lb.

Joining details of these clubs can be found in the Club section

Rother Fishery Association contact details:
Website www.fishingsussex.com
Secretary and fishery manager Mr. Vince Gould telephone 07776 031472
Postal address 13 Park Cottages, Hawkhurst, Kent. TN18 4HN
E-mail vince.gould@btinternet.com
Note: *The RFA do not allow night fishing on their water. 2 rods only.*

> Don't be in a rush to cast out, bait up and sit tight for a while for the carp to 'eye up' the food. Bites may well come quicker
>
> Lee Jackson

The Rother (Western)

The Rother (Western)

Sussex has 2 River Rother's; the Eastern and the Western. The Western begins life in the county of Hampshire, from its source at Empshott, just north of Petersfield. This is a non-tidal river. It enters Sussex at Durford Abbey Farm and passes through the villages of Dumpford, Chithurst, Iping and Stedham on the northern side of Midhurst before rolling on to Rotherbridge where it heads south towards Lower Fittleworth, then on to Stopham, where it joins the River Arun just south of the bridge. The total length is approximately 30 miles and it is partially fed by chalk springs from the south downs which give a stable and steady flow.

Clubs who control stretches of this river are as follows:

Pulborough Angling Society
Pulborough AS control approximately 1 mile of river at Hardham, near Pulborough. They control one bank only, on a stretch about 35 yards wide, that has a variety of depths. The club's record for carp here go to over 20lb. Night fishing is not allowed. 2 rods only.

Rother Angling Club
A narrow stretch of ¾ of a mile at North Mill near Midhurst is controlled by Rother AC. It is shallow in places and known to hold a few carp, although sizes are unknown. No night fishing. 2 rods only.

They also control a 1½ mile upstream stretch at Woolbeding, but that is said to hold no carp.

Petworth & Bognor Angling Club
This club controls about 7 miles of the Rother. The Coats Castle stretch is 2 miles of the south bank from Shopham Bridge almost down to Fittleworth. This section runs through open pasture with plenty of bankside cover and for many years was only fished by a small, game fishing syndicate. Petworth took control in June 2008 and are still looking for reports from members about the stock levels. It is known to hold quality specimens of barbel, chub, bream and some carp, although sizes are unknown.

The stretch at Shopham Bridge is a mile of both banks and holds lots of big chub and double figure barbel. Members have reported being frequently smashed up by large fish which are thought to be carp.

The club's 3 mile stretch of double bank at Fittleworth is full of fish of many species, including the odd carp well into double figures. This section has some deep swims as well as plenty of bankside cover.

The Coultershaw stretch and Mill Pool is 1 mile of bank. This lower section is earning a good reputation with the local anglers as a spot for a specimen, with carp into the high double figures and the chance of bigger fish. This stretch is close to the Hampshire border.

All sections of river do not allow night fishing. 2 rods only.

Joining details of these clubs can be found in the Club section of the book.

If you're on fish and struggling to get a bite, change your hook bait colour. A flash of colour can make a big difference

Ali Hamidi

This section is a bit of a mishmash, but all of these waters contain carp and are controlled by clubs whose memberships are open to all.

River Cuckmere

A small, narrow river with a variety of depths from 4 to 12 feet in places. It is tidal below Milton Lock, which is just above the village of Alfriston. The river rises near Heathfield and flows into the English Channel at Exceat, near the town of Seaford.

Clubs that control stretches of this river are as follows:

Seaford Angling Club

They control a stretch of water behind the club's Michelham Priory stillwater, which has produced carp up to 18lb. Night fishing is allowed. 2 rods only.

Southdown Angling Association

Members can fish upstream for about 1½ miles at Arlington and a short section from Shermans Bridge to Milton Street. Both these are non-tidal stretches that have produced a good number of carp to over 20lb. Night fishing is allowed. 2 rods only. Members only. No day tickets.

River Brede

A small, non-tidal river that runs north of Hastings to Winchelsea.

Clive Vale Angling Club

The Clive Vale AC has exclusive rights on a stretch of the Brede at Float Farm, near Snailham. It is a narrow part that has a standard depth of 4 to 6 feet. This small river has produced some good carp, with commons to 20lb and mirrors to 26lb. Night fishing is allowed. 2 rods only.

Chichester Canal

This 4 mile stretch of water is owned by the Chichester Ship Canal Trust. It contains a large head of fish, including a few carp in excess of 20lb. The well maintained tow paths give easy access to disabled anglers. The water can have all sorts of boat traffic, from rowing boats to charter cruises. The average depth of this brick bottomed canal is 5 feet. The area known as the Basin runs 8 to 10 feet deep and in the summer months the canal, which has quite a few lily pads, can get weedy.

Petworth & Bognor Angling Club

The Petworth & Bognor AC control 3 miles of canal. Night fishing is not allowed. 2 rods only. Two car parking areas are available.

Chichester Ship Canal Trust

This trust also controls fishing on the Chichester canal. A 52 week permit is available as well as day tickets.

Fees

Adult £45. OAP/Disabled/Junior (under 16) £25

Day tickets Adult £4. OAP/Disabled/Junior £2

Weekly ticket Adult £12. OAP/Disabled/Junior £7

Tickets available on the bank or from Trusts onsite shop.

Night fishing is allowed at the discretion of the bailiff.

2 rods only. Barbless hooks only.

Ship Canal Trust contact:

☎ 01243 771363

www.chichestercanal.org.uk

Royal Military Canal

Although the majority of this canal is in Kent, a small section is in Sussex at the Iden Lock area, where the canal meets the eastern River Rother before running onto Rye and the sea. The Iden Lock stretch is a known carp area.

This canal is 28 miles long and was entirely hand dug between 1804 and 1809. It is used for water level management of the Romney and Walland marshes. It is about 10 metres wide, with an average depth of 10 to 12 feet. It does get very weedy in the summer and water levels can change when the Iden Lock is opened. The carp stocks go back many years; it has taken stocks of carp in the 40's, 50's, 60's and 70's and as recently as 1984 500 mirrors were introduced by the then Southern Water Authority. The canal produced carp to 30lb+ in the 1970's and a Kent angling club claims today that fish in that bracket and bigger occupy their stretch of water, which is just a short distance from the Sussex stretch.

Sussex clubs that have rights on this canal are as follows:

Clive Vale Angling Club
Dorset Arms Angling Club
Rother Fishery Association
Hastings, Bexhill & District Angling Association

Pevensey Marshes

Pevensey Marshes is a large area of land between Bexhill and Pevensey, better known as havens or marsh drains. They are used to drain the land and were originally intended as a defence against Napoleon's army. Under normal weather conditions these waters have a slow, gentle flow but this can increase dramatically if flooding takes place "up country" and the gates are opened.

These drains can have deep water from 8 feet down to 15 feet and all the marsh waters contain a variety of coarse fish including roach, rudd, tench, bream, pike, perch, crucian carp and some good sized carp.

Southdown Angling Association

This association controls fishing on stretches of the Pevensey Haven, Raillands Ditch and the Chilly Stream. The Pevensey Haven is at Sheepwash and is joined upstream by the Chilly Stream. The Club fish the east bank of the Haven, which is approximately 15 yards wide with depths of 6 to 7 feet. This area has produced carp to over 20lb. The Chilly Stream can be fished on two banks, east and west, and is about the same width as the Haven but not quite as deep. This stream holds carp into double figures. Both these waters are heavily weeded from Spring through to late Autumn and can be gin clear.

Raillands Ditch can be fished two fields upstream and two fields downstream. This ditch is about 3½ metres wide with depths of 3 to 4 feet and has produced carp to over 20lb.

Night fishing is allowed on all these waters. 2 rods only.

Wallers Haven

To locals this is known as a marsh drain. This water is, on average, 7 metres wide with depths of 7 or 8 feet, plenty of weed and marginal reeds. The Haven runs north from Normans Bay near Eastbourne.

Clubs with fishing rights are as follows:

Southdown Angling Association

Southdown AA control stretches from Middle Bridge up to Boreham Street and this includes two banks at Ironbridge near Wartling. All of these stretches have produced carp with fish to 30lb from the Boreham area. This is a wide part that has depths of 7 to 8 feet. Middle Bridge is slightly deeper at 8 to 10 feet and access is said to be quite difficult in places. Night fishing is allowed. 2 rods only. These waters have a close season.

Hastings, Bexhill & District Angling Association

The Hastings and Bexhill Club share a stretch of the Wallers Haven with Southdown Angling Assocation. The shared area is one mile downstream at Boreham Street on the Eastbourne side. The club state that for those prepared to put the time in there are more carp present than most are aware of. Both commons and mirrors have been reportedly caught to over 20lb. There is easy parking at this stretch of the Wallers Haven.

Details of the clubs listed can be found in the Club section. Directions, rules and parking areas for all the clubs listed in this River section are also found in the club's membership handbooks.

Footnote

This river section was very difficult to put together as, unlike the stillwaters in our county, access to information is very limited. A huge thanks goes to all those club secretaries and bailiffs that were willing to help put this difficult section on paper.

The thing that struck me, was that nobody really knows what carp are swimming about in our rivers, so a big surprise could always be on the cards.

> First and last light are the best time to spot fish. Keep 'em peeled at dawn and dusk
>
> Danny Fairbrass

This small section gives details of venues that have, or allow, caravans onsite and holiday homes/cottages to let, and that also have some carp fishing available.

Alderwood Ponds

This West Sussex day ticket fishery has 2 caravans available for fishing breaks from 2 days to 7 days. One caravan is 2 berth and one is 4 berth and both have cooker, hob, fridge, TV and DVD as well as walk-in bathroom with shower.

The site also has 4 hook-up points for your own van or camper. Dogs are allowed but no children under the age of 12. There are 2 waters that both hold carp, with fish up to 38lb in Island Pond and 26lb in Corsican Pond.

For contact details see page 90 in the Day Ticket section. Prices on application.

Coghurst Hall

Set in 50 acres of woodlands, this lake is only fishable to those hiring deluxe caravans. A large lake with the biggest recorded carp weighing 26lb, the holiday park is near Hastings, East Sussex and bookings are made via a number of websites, including Hoseasons and Park Holidays.

☎ Hoseasons on 0844 8471180. Park holidays on 0845 8159775 or see websites.

Lakeside Holiday Park

This complex in Chichester, West Sussex has 10 lakes to fish on a day or weekly ticket. The site covers 150 acres and has facilities for camping, caravans with hook-up points and chalets, lodges and caravans for hire. The onsite facilities include swimming pool, paddling pool, shop, bistro and the Kingfisher Bar, plus other facilities. Open from 30th January to 16th January each year. All the lakes hold good sized carp.

For contact details see pages 102-105 in the Day Ticket section.

Menards Carp Fishery

This West Sussex fishery offers holidays from the bivvy for non members, from 5 days to 7 days. The lake holds very big carp. For contact details see page 110 in the Day Ticket section.

Merricks Fishery

This private fishery near Hastings in East Sussex has 2 holiday lets available. One sleeps 2 the other sleeps 3. The lake holds carp to over 30lb. For contact details see page 28 in the Day Ticket section.

Ninfield Holiday Cottages

Self catering cottages on a working farm near Battle in East Sussex. These are 4 star awarded holiday homes set in the South Downs with carp fishing at the nearby Rowallen fishery available. Rowallen has 2 lakes stocked with plenty of carp to 20lb. Price on application.

Contact details: www.ninfieldholidaycottages.co.uk

jill.godden2@fatinternet.com

☎ 01424 892686

Postal address: David and Jill Godden, Moor Hall Farm, Moor Hall Drive, Battle, Sussex TN33 9JT

Sumners Ponds

This fishery in West Sussex has a campsite for backpacking, touring by car, caravan or motor home. There are superb facilities including a shop, amenity block and cafe. Pitches have electric hook-up and cable TV plus many other facilities. There are 4 premium pitches with chalets on the big pond, which holds carp to over 30lb. For contact details see page 120 in the Day Ticket section.

Three Ponds Holiday Park and Fishery

This holiday park in East Sussex has been owned by David and Joanne Barlow since 2000, both are actively involved in the day to day running of this private park, which has been awarded the prestigious David Bellamy Gold Conservation Award and the Green Tourism Gold Award. Ideally situated for visiting Eastbourne, Brighton and the historic town of Lewes, it also has some onsite carp fishing. It has a pond exclusively for the use of those in the holiday homes, with plenty of carp into double figures. Visitors may also fish the 2 other ponds, one of which has carp up to 26lb.

For details ☎ 01273 513530 – www.threepondspark.co.uk

Wylands International Angling Centre

Wylands in East Sussex not only has 10 waters to fish, but also has facilities for touring and camping, as well as chalets and static caravans for hire. There are many onsite facilities including toilets, showers and a cafe which has long opening hours. Weekly and day tickets are available and the complex holds carp to over 30lb. For contact details see page 46 in the Day Ticket section.

Directory of Tackle Shops

Aldwick Angling
25 Nyewood Lane, Aldwick, Bognor Regis,
West Sussex PO21 2QB
☎ 01243 829054
www.aldwickangling.com
Opening Hours: Mon-Sat 8am – 6pm. Sun 8am – 12 noon

Anglers Den
6 North Road, Pevensey Bay, Pevensey,
East Sussex BN24 6AY
☎ 01323 360441
Opening Hours: Open 7.30 am every day. Check for closing
times on specific days.

Anglers Cabin
8 St. Mary's Walk, High Street, Hailsham,
East Sussex BN27 1AN
☎ 01323 440344
www.anglers-cabin.com
Opening Hours: Mon-Fri 9am – 5.30pm. Sat 8.30am – 5.30pm

A.R. Tackle
8 Castle Street, Hastings, East Sussex TN34 3DY
☎ 01424 422094
Opening Hours: Mon-Sat 9am – 5.15pm

Arun Angling
The Old Blacksmiths Yard, Water Lane, Angmering,
West Sussex BN16 4EP
☎ 01903 770099
www.arunangling.co.uk
Opening Hours: Mon-Fri 8.30am – 5.15pm. Sat 8am – 5.15pm

Angling Specialists Horsham (Ash)
29 Queen Street, Horsham, West Sussex RH13 5AA
☎ 01403 264644
Opening Hours: Mon-Sat 8am – 5.30pm

Burgess Hill Angling Centre
143 Lower Church Road, Burgess Hill, West Sussex RH15 9AB
☎ 01444 232287
www.burgesshillanglingcentre.co.uk
Opening Hours: Mon-Fri 9am – 5.30pm. Sat 9am – 5pm

Crowborough Tackle
The Broadway, Crowborough, East Sussex TN6 1DF
☎ 01892 667671
www.crowboroughtackle.co.uk
Opening Hours: Tues-Fri 9am – 6pm. Sat 9am – 5.30pm

Hastings Angling Centre
33 The Bourne, Hastings, East Sussex TN34 3AY
☎ 01424 432178
www.hastingsangling.co.uk
Opening Hours: Mon-Sat 8am – 5.30pm. Sun 8am – 12 noon

Hook, Line & Sinker
54 Sackville Road, Bexhill-on-Sea, East Sussex TN39 3JE
☎ 01424 733211
Opening Hours: Open Daily at 8.30am (apart from Weds).
Call for daily closing times.

Jack Frost Tackle
Reynolds Place, Crawley, West Sussex RH11 7HB
☎ 01293 521186
www.jfonline.co.uk
Opening Hours: Mon-Sat 9am – 6pm. Sun 9am – 1pm
(Summer)

Lagoon Tackle & Bait
327 Kingsway, Hove, East Sussex BN3 4LD
☎ 01273 415879
Opening Hours: Open Daily at 8.30am. Call for closing times.

M A Wickham
4 Middle Row, East Grinstead, West Sussex RH19 3AX
☎ 01342 305095
Opening Hours: Mon-Sat 8.30am – 5.30pm

Percy's of Lewes
9 Cliffe High Street, Lewes, East Sussex BN7 2AH
☎ 01273 473207
Opening Hours: Mon-Sat 8.30am – 5pm. Wed close 4pm

Polegate Angling Centre
101 Station Road, Polegate, East Sussex BN26 6EB
☎ 01323 486379
Opening Hours: Mon-Sat 9am – 5pm (6pm Fri)
Sun 9am – 1pm June – end August.

Prime Angling
74 Brighton Road, Worthing, West Sussex BN11 2EN
☎ 01903 821594
Opening Hours: Mon-Sat 8.30am – 5pm. Sun 8am – 12 noon.

The Rye Angling Centre
5A Market Road, Rye, East Sussex TN31 7JA
☎ 01797 227779
www.ryeangling.co.uk
Opening Hours: Mon-Sat 9am – 5pm (1pm Tues)
Sun 10am – 3pm

Southern Angling Specialists (SAS)
2 Stockbridge Place, Stockbridge Road, Chichester, West
Sussex PO19 8QH
☎ 01243 531669
Opening Hours: Mon-Sat 8am – 5.30pm (5pm Tues)
Sun 8am – 12 noon (Closed Sun Xmas to Easter)

S. H. Tackle
58 Bohemia Road, St. Leonards-on-Sea,
East Sussex TN37 6RQ
☎ 01424 431583
Opening Hours: Mon-Sat 9am – 5pm (1pm Wed)
Sun 9am – 11.30am

Shoreline Angling
7 Shore Road, East Wittering, West Sussex PO20 8DY
☎ 01243 673353
Opening Hours: Mon-Sat 9am – 5pm (1pm Wed)
Sun 9am – 3pm (Summer only)

Squires Fishing Tackle
25 Southwick Square, Southwick, Brighton,
East Sussex BN42 4PF
☎ 01273 592903
Opening Hours: Mon-Sat 8.30am – 5pm (6pm Fri)

Steve's Tackle
38 White Rock, Hastings, East Sussex TN34 1JL
☎ 01424 433404
www.stevestackle.co.uk
Opening Hours: Mon-Sat 8.30am – 5pm

Sussex Angling Supplies
The Old Printworks, Streatfield Road, Heathfield, East Sussex
TN21 8LA
☎ 01435 868938
Opening Hours: Open daily at 7.30am. Call for closing times.
(Times change in Winter)

The Peacehaven Angler
135 South Coast Road, Peacehaven, East Sussex BN10 8PA
☎ 01273 586000
Opening Hours: Mon-Thurs 8am – 6pm
Fri-Sat 7.30am – 6.45pm (Closed Wed)
Sun 8am – 1pm

The Tackle Warehouse
Unit 14, Rutherford Way, Crawley, West Sussex RH10 9RD
☎ 01293 550907
www.tacklewarehouse.co.uk
Opening Hours: Mon-Thurs 9am – 5.30pm (6pm Fri)
Sat 7.30am – 5.30pm (1pm Sun)

Tidal Angling
81 Lower Street, Pulborough, West Sussex RH20 2BP
☎ 01798 873790
Opening Hours: Daily 8am – 5.30pm
(Closed all day Thurs & Sun)

Tony's Tackle
211 Seaside, Eastbourne, East Sussex BN22 7NP
☎ 01323 739562 / 731388
Opening Hours: Mon-Sat 8.30am – 6pm
Sun 8.30am – 12 noon

Tropicana
5-6 Pier Road, Littlehampton, West Sussex BN17 5BA
☎ 01903 715190
Opening Hours: Mon-Fri 8.30 – 5pm. Sat 7.30 – 5pm
(12.45pm Sun)

Uckfield Angling Centre
212A High Street, Uckfield, East Sussex TN22 1RD
☎ 01825 760300
www.uckfieldangling.com
Opening Hours: Mon-Thurs & Sat 9am – 5.30pm (6pm Fri)

Miscellaneous

This section is about waters that all contain a few carp but where detailed information is both sparse and hard to obtain. These waters include council run venues, private lakes and day ticket waters, in fact any water that is said to be home to a few carp.

Back Arun Fishery

Two lakes near Arundel in West Sussex which allows day fishing only. Tickets are available on the bank. Both lakes hold carp up to 18lb as well as other species.

Malcolm Penn ☎ 01903 721546

Cuckfield Fishery

This fishery comprises 3 small lakes on private land, just outside the village in West Sussex. Depths go down to 12 feet and all ponds hold mirror carp, although sizes are unknown. Day tickets are available. No night fishing. Barbless hooks must be used. There is also an onsite cafe.

☎ 01444 459999

Ditchling Common Ponds

Two lakes run by East Sussex County Council, the larger pond is said to hold carp to 30lb, the smaller water holds carp to double figures. They have a traditional close season, and season tickets are available.

Contact the council offices.
Ken McManaman on ☎ 01273 482670

Hailsham Country Park Lake

Run by the local East Sussex Town Council, this water offers day tickets, weekly junior tickets and a season permit. It has a traditional close season and is said to hold carp to over 30lb.

All details through the local council offices, Market Square, Hailsham.

☎ 01323 841702

Somerset Fishery

This West Sussex water in the Worthing area is run by the Environment Agency and is said to hold carp into double figures and a few possible twenties. ☎ 01903 871606

Thornden Pond

Day tickets are available on this small pond near Battle in East Sussex and its home to some very wild commons into double figures. No night fishing.

Paul Plumley ☎ 01435 830586

The Sussex Piscatorial Society

Membership to this society is hard to come by and extremely limited. The SPS runs several coarse fisheries across Sussex and do have waters that hold some good sized carp. It has a very strict code of conduct and references regarding applicants angling history may be required.

All enquiries are through the website only
www.sussexpiscatorialsociety.co.uk

Isfield & District Angling Club

This is probably the biggest club in the county when it comes to the number of venues available to its members. It has a number of waters that hold carp but states that it is not a carp fishing club.

All membership details from M.A. Wickham Fishing Tackle in East Grinstead (see tackle shop section on page 218 for details).

Carshalton & District Angling Society

As the name suggests, this is a Surrey club but they do control the rights to 2 lakes in Sussex – see *Bury St Austins Lakes below.*

Bury St Austins Lakes

2 waters on private farmland in Rudgwick, East Sussex. The large lake has 40 swims and the top lake 25. Described as the place to go after you have blanked elsewhere, both waters are stocked with plenty of small carp up to double figures. No night fishing allowed.

Contact details:
www.carshaltonanddistrictanglingsociety.co.uk

Stuart Edwards ☎ 0208 669 7304

CALPAC – (Central Association of London Provincial Angling Clubs)

A number of Sussex Clubs are affiliated to this association, giving exchange memberships which allow fishing on other waters in other counties. CALPAC have a couple of venues in Sussex:

The River Arun

CALPAC control a 1½ mile stretch of the river at Swan Bridge, near Pulborough in West Sussex. Day tickets are available. This stretch of the Arun does hold carp.

Balls Green Lakes

CALPAC control the rights to these waters near Withyham in East Sussex. There are 2 lakes, the biggest of about 2 acres holds commons and mirrors into high double figures, the smaller water is said to be carpless. No night fishing. 2 rods only. No boilies. Members only.

Membership to CALPAC:

Details on website www.calpac.info.co.uk

Club secretary Mr Malcolm Milford-Scott.

☎ (before 8pm) on 0208 645 6820

The Carp Society
www.thecarpsociety.com
info@thecarpsociety.com
☎ 01367 253959
Horseshoe Lake, Burford Road, Lechlade, Glouchestershire
GL7 3QQ

British carp study group
www.bcsg.org.uk
Membership Secretary: 01664 857995

English Carp Heritage Organisation (ECHO)
www.echo.co.uk
carp@hotmail.com
☎ 01252 861955
Fax 01252 873123
c/o Yateley Angling Centre, 16 The Parade, Yateley, Hampshire
GU46 7UN

Angling Trust
www.anglingtrust.net
admin@anglingtrust.net
☎ 0844 7700616
Fax 0115 906 1251
Eastwood House, 6 Rainbow Street, Leominster,
Herefordshire HR6 8DQ

Environment Agency
www.environment-agency.gov.uk
enquiries@environment-agency-gov.uk
☎ 08708 506506
☎ 0800 807060 (Pollution Hotline)
☎ 0800 807060 (Illegal Fish Movements)
PO Box 544, Rotherham, Yorkshire S60 1BY

Centre For Environment, Fisheries & Aquaculture Science
(CEFAS)
www.cefas.co.uk
☎ 01305 206681

Institute Of Fisheries Management
www.ifm.org.uk
info@ifm.org.uk
☎ 0115 982 2318
Fax 0115 982 6150
22 Rushworth Avenue, West Bridgford, Nottingham
NG2 7LF

RSPB
www.rspb.org.uk
☎ 01273 775333

The Swan Sanctuary
www.theswansanctuary.org.uk
☎ 01932 240790

Bexhill Wildlife Trust
Vet on call 24 hours for water bird problems
☎ 01424 210788

Carp Fishing Magazine Contacts

Carpworld & Crafty Carper
www.anglingpublications.co.uk
info@anglingpublications.co.uk
☎ 0114 258 0812
Fax 0114 258 2728
101 Broadfield Road, Sheffield S8 0XH

Big Carp
www.bigcarpmagazine.co.uk
info@bigcarpmagazine.co.uk
☎ 01252 373658
44 Herbs End, Cove, Hampshire GU14 9YD

Carpology
www.carpology.net
studio@carpology.net
☎ 01502 575788

Advanced Carp Fishing & Total Carp
www.totalcarpmagazine.com
marccoulson@dhpub.co.uk
☎ 01327 311999
Fax 01327 311190

Carp Talk
www.carptalk-online.co.uk
carper@btconnect.com
☎ 01430 440624
Fax 01430 441319
Carp Talk, Newport, East Yorkshire HU15 2QS

Freespool
james@freespoolcarmag.com
☎ 01962 883328
☎ 07748 825027 (James Harrison)

Angling Tuition
Smart Carping
www.smartcarping.com
☎ 07864 959163 (Ian Gemson)

'There are no new waters to fish, they've all been found!'

I used to think that way until I started to put this book together, but it wasn't long before I realised that, in fact, there are waters all over the place that I'd never heard of in this wonderful county of Sussex, and I have only scratched the surface.

One of the first things that I did was to buy an AA Street by Street Map of Sussex, and I was shocked at the amount of blue there was on the pages; some which I knew of, but many which I didn't. There are even waters behind roads that I'd driven along many a time, without giving it a thought.

So, if you think there are no new waters to explore, think again. Look hard and you will be very surprised – you may just find your own little haven in untapped Sussex.

Index

Index

Index

The Author

Clive Williams is 56 years old and has spent the last fifty years living in Horsham, West Sussex. He has been carp fishing for over thirty years and after cutting his teeth on local, Sussex waters, he moved up to the Colne Valley and fished the famous Longfield Lake in the early '80's, alongside the likes of Ritchie McDonald, Pete Springate and Rob Maylin. Then, in the late '80's he began his long term love affair with Savay Lake, where he is still a member today.

He wrote a fishing column in the West Sussex County Times in the late '80's, and was the founder member of the Sussex branch of the CAA in the early '80's, and some of his meetings at Horsham Football Club have become legendary!

He has been married to Jo for 25 years and although they have no children they do have their dog, Zola (yes, Clive is a Chelsea supporter).

These days he is a freelance tackle agent, but he does also have an inventive side and, indeed, it was he who invented the Korda Krusha, amongst other things.

Through all of that, though, his love of Sussex and its carp waters has never waned, hence this labour of love. We hope you find as much enjoyment in this beautiful county of Sussex as Clive has – we're sure you will.